Chr

with Jane Hudson

ENGLISH FILE

Pre-Intermediate Workbook with key

OXFORD
UNIVERSITY PRESS

Paul Seligson and Clive Oxenden are the original co-authors of
English File 1 and *English File 2*

Contents

Practise listening out of class

For Workbook audio, go to
www.oup.com/elt/englishfile

Select your level.

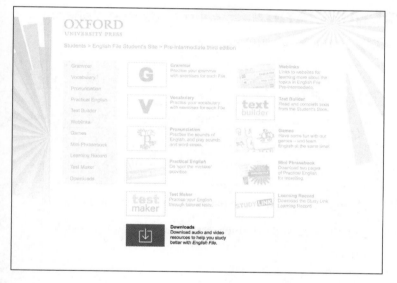

Select **Downloads**.

Select **Audio: Workbook**.

1A Where are you from?

1 GRAMMAR word order in questions

a Put the word into the correct place in the questions.

1 Where you born? (were)

   Where **were** you born?

2 Do have any brothers or sisters? (you)

   _____

3 What university you go to? (do)

   _____

4 What languages you speak? (can)

   _____

5 Where you study English before? (did)

   _____

6 What kind of music do you listen? (to)

   _____

7 How do you do exercise? (often)

   _____

8 Where did you last weekend? (go)

   _____

b Write questions in the present or past simple.

1 Where _do you go to university_ ?
   (you / go to university)

2 What _____?
   (you / do last night)

3 What _____?
   (TV programmes / your girlfriend / watch)

4 When _____?
   (your birthday)

5 Where _____?
   (you / from)

6 Where _____?
   (your friends / go / holiday last year)

7 What kind of books _____?
   (you / read)

8 Why _____?
   (you / angry yesterday)

2 VOCABULARY common verb phrases

Match the verbs and nouns.

1	be born	j	a	MTV, a TV series
2	do	☐	b	in a house, with friends
3	listen to	☐	c	two sisters, a pet
4	play	☐	d	exercise, sport
5	read	☐	e	an email, a magazine
6	speak	☐	f	to the cinema, on holiday
7	live	☐	g	the guitar, basketball
8	watch	☐	h	a foreign language, English
9	go	☐	i	dance music, R&B
10	have	☐	j	in Kraków, in Poland

3 PRONUNCIATION vowel sounds, the alphabet

a Circle the letter with a different vowel sound.

1 eɪ train	2 eɪ train	3 iː tree	4 iː tree	5 e egg	6 e egg	7 uː boot
A	H	G	M	N	X	Q
K	P	V	C	B	S	I
Ⓔ	J	R	D	F	K	U

b ◉ 1.1 Listen and check. Then listen again and repeat the letters.

c Under<u>line</u> the stressed syllables in these words.

1 in|stru|ment
2 pro|gramme
3 thir|teen
4 thir|ty
5 u|ni|ver|si|ty
6 week|end
7 ma|ga|zine
8 sis|ter
9 lan|guage
10 a|ddress

d ◉ 1.2 Listen and check. Then listen again and repeat the words.

4 SPELLING AND NUMBERS

a Continue the series.

1 nine, ten, _____*eleven*_____, _____*twelve*_____
2 fifteen, sixteen, _____, _____
3 sixty, seventy, _____, _____
4 ninety-eight, ninety-nine, _____, _____
5 six hundred, seven hundred, _____, _____
6 three hundred and fifty, four hundred, _____, _____
7 one thousand, three thousand, _____, _____
8 ten thousand, twenty thousand, _____, _____

b 🔊 **1.3** Listen and write the words.

1 _____*parents*_____   6 _____
2 _____   7 _____
3 _____   8 _____
4 _____   9 _____
5 _____   10 _____

5 LISTENING

a 🔊 **1.4** Listen to a conversation between two people at a party. Why does Ben leave?

_____

b Listen again. Mark the sentences T (true) or F (false).

1 Sandra is a nurse.   *T*
2 Ben is a doctor.   —
3 Sandra likes dance music.   —
4 Sandra didn't go to the Muse concert.   —
5 Sandra plays tennis.   —
6 Ben plays football.   —

USEFUL WORDS AND PHRASES

Learn these words and phrases.

get in touch with /get ɪn tʌtʃ wɪð/
go to bed early /gəʊ tə bed ˈɜːli/
have (sth) in common /hæv ɪn ˈkɒmən/
last weekend /lɑːst wiːkˈend/
spend time on (sth) /spend taɪm ɒn/
somewhere nice /ˈsʌmweə naɪs/
How often do you…? /haʊ ˈɒfn də ju/
What kind of (music)…? /wɒt ˈkaɪnd ɒv/
Where were you born? /ˈweə wə ju ˈbɔːn/

A true friend is someone who is there for you when
he / she would prefer to be somewhere else.
Len Wein, American comic book writer

1B Charlotte's choice

1 GRAMMAR present simple

a Write negative sentences.

1 You get up early. *You don't get up early* .
2 It rains a lot here. It doesn't rain a lot here .
3 We live in a flat. We don't live in a flat .
4 I play tennis. I don't play tennis .
5 He has a beard. He doesn't a beard .
6 They go to the gym. They don't go to the gym
7 She writes a blog. She doesn't write a blog

b Complete the questions with *do* or *does*.

1 When __do__ you meet your friends?
2 __Does__ your laptop have a webcam?
3 What time __do__ we need to leave?
4 __Does__ your mother work from home?
5 Which websites __do__ you use most?
6 __Does__ your girlfriend like action films?
7 __Does__ your brother spend a long time on Facebook?

c Complete the text with the correct form of the verbs in the box.

~~not come~~ earn get on study have ~~not like~~ live
prefer ~~not see~~ share want ~~work~~

I am very different from
my boyfriend, Jamie. Jamie
[1] __works__ as a vet and he
[2] __earns__ quite a lot
of money. I'm a student and
I [3] __study__ music at
university. I [4] __want__
to be a music teacher when
I finish.

Jamie [5] __lives__ in a small house in the country,
and I [6] __share__ a flat with some friends in the
city centre. We often [7] __have__ parties in our
flat, but Jamie [8] __doesn't come__ . He's quite shy, so he
[9] __doesn't like__ being with other people. I'm quite
extrovert so I [10] __prefer__ to be in a group.
I [11] __don't see__ Jamie much because he's usually busy.
But when we're together, we always [12] __get on__ really
well. Some people say that opposites attract, and for Jamie
and me, it's true.

2 VOCABULARY describing people

appearance

a Complete the sentences.

1 Does your boyfriend have br__own__ eyes or bl__ue__ eyes?
2 Tanya's dad doesn't have any hair. He's
   b__ald__ .
3 My best friend's hair isn't str__aight__ . It's
   c__urly__ .
4 Andy doesn't shave. He has a b__eard__ and a
   m__oustache__ .
5 You aren't f__at__ at all. I think you're quite
   sl__im__ .
6 When Jake was young, he was very th__in__
   but now he's a bit ov__erweight__ .
7 My hair isn't brown, it's r__ed__ . And I'm
   not short, I'm m__edium__ h__ight__ .

b Match the questions 1–6 with the answers a–f.

1 What did you look like when you were a child? [c]
2 What does your husband look like? [d]
3 What's your girlfriend like? [e]
4 What does your sister look like? [a]
5 What's George like? [b]
6 What were you like when you were at school? [f]

a She's tall and slim with long blond hair.
b He's very kind and quite hard-working.
c I had short curly hair and I was overweight.
d He has short dark hair and a moustache.
e She's very clever and quite extrovert.
f I was very talkative and a bit lazy.

personality

c Complete the opposites.

1 talkative   __quiet__
2 shy   extravert
3 generous   mean
4 friendly   unfriendly
5 hard-working   lazy
6 kind   unkind
7 serious   funny
8 stupid   intelligent / clever .

3 PRONUNCIATION final -s / -es

a 🔊 1.5 Listen and (circle) the verb with a different sound.

1 ![snake] snake	2 ![snake] snake	3 ![zebra] zebra	4 ![zebra] zebra	5 /ɪz/	6 /ɪz/
works laughs (watches)	lives thinks drinks	knows rains likes	runs starts goes	leaves dresses washes	teaches cooks misses

b Listen again and repeat the words.

c Under<u>line</u> the stressed syllable.

1 talk|a|tive
2 ex|tro|vert
3 un|friend|ly
4 ge|ne|rous
5 mou|stache
6 se|ri|ous
7 cur|ly
8 qui|et
9 o|ver|weight

d 🔊 1.6 Listen and check. Then listen again and repeat the words.

4 READING

a Read the article. What happens on 'Singles' Day' in Shanghai?

'Singles' Day' in Shanghai

11 November is 'Singles' Day' in Shanghai, and every year a dating event takes place where all the single men and women of the city have the chance to meet a partner. Last year, it was so popular that the organizers had to close online registration because there were no more places.

Between 10,000 and 40,000 people attend the event every year. It's <u>held</u> in a district of Shanghai called Thames Town. At least 50 dating agencies take part. They <u>set up stands</u> in the town hall with billboards displaying cards with the height, birth date, education, and annual income of thousands of clients. People who did not manage to register for the event organize their own unofficial dating system by writing their names and phone numbers on bits of paper and attaching them to the <u>fence</u> outside the town hall.

More people take part in 'Singles' Day' every year because of the growing number of single adults in Shanghai. In the centre of the city, more than 24% of people over the age of 15 are unmarried.

b Read the article again. Mark the sentences T (true) or F (false).

1 The people who take part in 'Singles' Day' aren't married. _T_

2 Many people register for the event on the internet. T

3 All of the dating events are in the town hall. T

4 People who don't register for the event can't find a partner on 'Singles' Day'. F

5 Every year, there are more single adults in Shanghai. T

c <u>Underline</u> five words you don't know. Check their meaning and pronunciation with a dictionary.

5 LISTENING

a 🔊 1.7 Listen to a radio programme about online dating. How many people call the programme? _____

b Listen again and match the callers with the sentences A–F.

1 Alan _C_ E
2 Kate _E_ A
3 Paolo _B_ D

A He / She doesn't have time for a social life.
B He / She made a mistake.
C ~~He / She had a child with the partner he / she met online.~~
D He / She married someone who was married before.
E He / She doesn't like meeting new people.
F He / She is happily married now, but doesn't have any children.

USEFUL WORDS AND PHRASES

Learn these words and phrases.

guy /gaɪ/
partner /ˈpɑːtnə/
single person /ˈsɪŋɡl ˈpɜːsn/
smile /smaɪl/
sociable /ˈsəʊʃəbl/
be into (sth) /bi ˈɪntə/
feel like (doing sth) /fiːl laɪk/
get on well (with) /ɡet ɒn wel/
go on a date /ɡəʊ ɒn ə deɪt/
sense of humour /sens ɒv ˈhjuːmə/

1 VOCABULARY

clothes

a Complete the crossword.

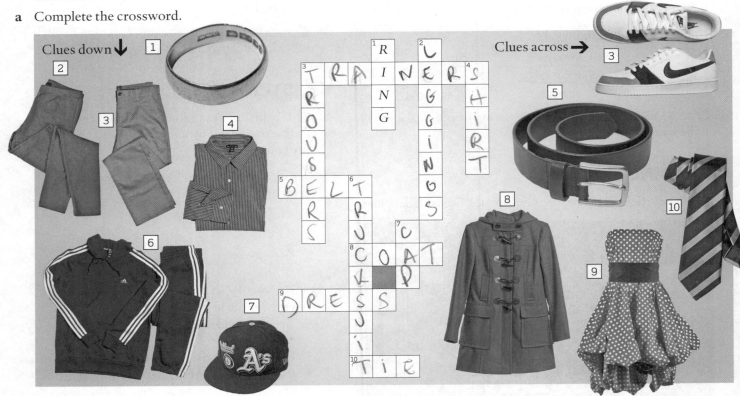

Clues down ↓

Clues across →

Crossword answers:
- 1 down: RING
- 3 across: TRAINERS
- 2 down: LEGGINGS
- 4 down: SHIRT
- 3 down: TROUSERS
- 5 across: BELT
- 6 down: TRUNKS
- 7 down: CAP / CARDIGAN
- 8 across: COAT
- 9 across: DRESS
- 10 across: TIE

prepositions of place

b Look at the painting. Complete the sentences with these prepositions.

~~on the left~~ in ~~between~~ ~~behind~~
~~in front of~~ ~~next to~~

1 There are many people ___*in*___ the picture.
2 There are some boats
  ___on the left___ of the picture.
3 There are two small animals
  ___in front of___ the woman
  and man with an umbrella.
4 A small girl in a white dress is
  ___next to___ the woman in
  the middle of the painting.
5 A black dog is ___behind___
  the man with a beard.
6 There is a woman ___between___
  the two men sitting down.

2 GRAMMAR present continuous

a Look at the painting again. Read the museum guide's description of it. Write the verbs in the present continuous.

Sunday Afternoon on the Island of La Grande Jatte, 1884-86, Georges Pierre Seurat

As you can see, the sun [1] *is shining* in this picture, and the people [2] are relaxing (relax) by the river Seine in Paris. On the right of the picture, a man and a woman [3] are walking (walk) their dogs. On the left, a man [4] is lieing (lie) on the grass. He looks like he [5] 's relaxing (relax). In the middle of the picture, two girls [6] are sitting (sit) down. What [7] are they doing (they / do)? Maybe they [8] are waiting (wait) for some friends? Or perhaps they [9] are watching (watch) the other people? On the right, near the trees, there is another girl. She [10] is playing (play), but we can't see who with.

b Complete the sentences with the present simple or present continuous form of the verbs in the box.

~~drink~~ drive ~~like~~ ~~listen~~ ~~live~~ ~~rain~~ ~~sleep~~ ~~study~~ ~~wear~~ ~~work~~

1 Sorry, I can't hear you. I*'m listening* to music.
2 Charles always __drives__ to work.
3 'Shhhh! Be quiet! The children are sleeping .'
4 We can't play tennis today. It 's raining .
5 Fiona __drinks__ four cups of coffee every day.
6 We __like__ this picture very much.
7 My brother __is working__ for Apple.
8 Kathy always __wears__ jeans at home.
9 They can't come to the theatre because they are studying for the exam tomorrow.
10 My parents __live__ in a big house in the country.

3 PRONUNCIATION /ə/ and /ɜː/

a Write the words in the chart.

~~cardigan~~ ~~fashion~~ ~~prefer~~ ~~sandals~~ ~~shirt~~ ~~skirt~~ ~~sweater~~ ~~trainers~~ ~~trousers~~ ~~T-shirt~~ ~~third~~ ~~world~~

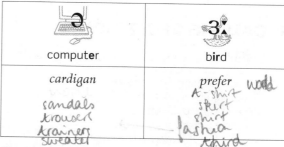 ə computer	ɜː bird
cardigan sandals trouser trainers sweater	*prefer* world t-shirt skirt shirt fashion third

b ◑ **1.8** Listen and check. Then listen again and repeat the words.

4 LISTENING

a ◑ **1.9** Listen to an advert for an art exhibition. What is special about the pictures?

b Listen again and answer the questions.

1 Where is the David Hockney exhibition?

2 What was the first picture he drew on his iPhone?

3 What does he do with his flower pictures?

4 When is the last day of the exhibition?

5 How much does the exhibition cost?

USEFUL WORDS AND PHRASES

Learn these words and phrases.

feet /fiːt/ singulier foot : pluriel
knee /niː/
portrait /ˈpɔːtreɪt/
poster /ˈpəʊstə/
pregnant /ˈpregnənt/
relationship /rɪˈleɪʃnʃɪp/
unusual /ʌnˈjuːʒuəl/
close together /kləʊs təˈgeðə/

9

1 CALLING RECEPTION

Complete the conversation with the phrases in the box.

I have a problem with the Wi-Fi.
I'll put you through to IT.
I'll send somebody up right away.
I'm sorry to bother you again.
There's a problem with the shower.
~~This is room 402.~~

A Hello, reception.
B Hello. ¹ _This is room 402._
A How can I help you?
B ² _____. There isn't any hot water.
A I'm sorry, madam. ³ _____.
B Thank you.

A Good morning, reception.
B Hello. ⁴ _____. This is room 402.
A How can I help you?
B ⁵ _____. I can't get a signal.
A I'm sorry, madam. ⁶ _____.
B Thanks.

2 SOCIAL ENGLISH

Complete the missing words in the conversation.

1 A So, here you are at _last_.
  B Yes. It's great to be here.

2 A Do you have a g_reat_ v_iew_____?
  B Yes. I can see the Empire State Building from my window.

3 A William is l_____ f_____ to meeting you.
  B Really? Who's William?

4 A It's time to go. You m_ust_ be_____ really tired.
  B I guess you're right.

5 A B_y_ t_he_ w_ay_, it's great to see you again.
  B Yes. It's great to see you, too.

3 READING

a Read the advert and mark the sentences T (true) or F (false).

1 The Park Central New York is in the centre of the city.   T
2 It's near major tourist attractions.   T
3 It's very comfortable.   T
4 All rooms have free Wi-Fi access.   F
5 The hotel's restaurant is not very expensive.   T
6 The hotel has a free car park.   F
7 The staff only speak English.   F

Park Central New York Hotel
New York

Our facilities and services:
- in-room safe
- in-room Wi-Fi (surcharge)
- electronic check-out
- parking garage (surcharge)
- room service
- on-site car rental
- giftshop

'Great location and service'

Located in the heart of the city, the Park Central New York is in easy walking distance of Carnegie Hall, Broadway and the Museum of Modern Art (MOMA). Central Park is only three blocks away and Fifth Avenue, with its international boutiques and huge department stores, is only a ten-minute walk from the hotel. For guests who want to travel further away, there are seven subway lines located within three blocks of the hotel.

The Park Central New York offers great service, great comfort and great value. The hotel's bistro, 'Cityhouse', provides the perfect setting for dinner before a concert or a Broadway show in the evening. Guests can enjoy the reasonably priced set menu while watching the world go by on Seventh Avenue through the bistro's oversized windows. There's also a bar in the lobby where guests can enjoy a cocktail after the show.

Because of its central location, the Park Central New York is the ideal hotel for tourists visiting the city for the first time. Our multilingual staff on the front desk are always happy to provide tour assistance and answer any questions guests may have.

b Underline five words you don't know. Use your dictionary to look up their pronunciation and meaning.

2A Right place, wrong person

1 VOCABULARY holidays

a Write the phrases.

1 __*go*__ camping
2 go __*for*__ a __*walk*__
3 __*book*__ flights on the internet
4 go __*abroad*__
5 ~~go~~ __*hire*__ skis
6 go __*out*__ at night
7 __*stay*__ in a hotel
8 go __*sightseeing*__
9 ~~go~~ on the beach __*sunbathen*__
10 go ~~away~~ __*f*__ for the weekend

b Complete the sentences with an adjective.

1 We loved our room. It was very c<u>omfortable</u>.
2 The weather was warm and s<u>unny</u> every day.
3 There were a lot of people everywhere. It was very cr<u>owded</u>.
4 We ate very well. The food was d<u>elicious</u>.
5 The staff in the hotel were horrible. They were very unh<u>elpful</u>, and sometimes quite rude.
6 There wasn't much in the apartment. It was very b<u>asic</u>. It didn't even have a fridge.
7 The other people on the trip were very fr<u>iendly</u>. We hope to meet some of them again in the future.
8 The town was l<u>ovely</u>. All the houses had flowers on the balcony and were painted different colours.
9 It was cl<u>oudy</u> and we didn't see the sun at all.
10 Our first meal was d<u>isgusting</u>, so we didn't eat at the hotel again.

2 GRAMMAR past simple: regular and irregular verbs

a Write the past simple of these verbs in the correct column.

argue ~~begin~~ ~~arrive~~ ask ~~buy~~ ~~can~~ ~~choose~~ ~~eat~~ ~~feel~~ invite ~~rent~~ ~~say~~ stay ~~sunbathe~~

Regular	Irregular
argued	*began*
asked	bought
arrived	could
sunbathed	said
rented	~~chose~~ chose
invited	ate
stayed	felt

b Make the verbs negative.

1 We stayed at a campsite.
   __*We didn't stay*__ in a hotel.
2 They bought postcards.
   __They didn't buy__ any souvenirs.
3 The people were unfriendly.
   __The people didn't ~~is~~ weren't__ very helpful.
4 I sunbathed on the beach.
   __I didn't sunbath__ by the pool.
5 We hired bikes.
   __We didn't hire__ a car.
6 He spent a month in Bangkok.
   __He didn't spend__ a week there.
7 Our room was dirty.
   __Our room ~~didn't is~~ wasn't__ very clean.

11

c Complete the text with the past simple form of the verbs in the box.

~~arrive~~ ~~ask~~ ~~book~~ ~~cannot~~ ~~decide~~ go (x2) ~~look~~ ~~take~~ ~~want~~

The holiday that wasn't

Four years ago, we ¹ _decided_ to go away for the weekend. We
² _wanted_ to go to Portugal, so we ³ _booked_ a beautiful
apartment online. A week later, we ⁴ _took_ a taxi to the
airport. We ⁵ _arrived_ at the airport at two o'clock, and we
⁶ _went_ to check in. The woman at the desk ⁷ _asked_
us for our passports. We ⁸ _looked_ in our bags, but we
⁹ _couldn't_ find them. So we ¹⁰ _went_ home!

---

d Read the text in **c** again. Complete the questions.

1 When _did they decide_ to go away for the weekend? Four years ago.
2 Where _did they went_ to go? Portugal.
3 How _did they book_ the apartment? They booked it online.
4 When _did they arrive_ at the airport? At two o'clock.
5 What _did she_ ask for? She asked for their passports.
6 Where _did the happen_ in the end? They went back home.

3 PRONUNCIATION -ed endings, irregular verbs

a 🔊 2.1 Listen and (circle) the verb which has a different -ed sound.

1 walked   asked   (rented)
2 argued   (wanted)   stayed
3 (booked)   started   decided
4 arrived   (invited)   sunbathed

b Listen again and repeat the words.

c Write these irregular past simple forms in the correct circle.

~~bought~~ ~~broke~~ ~~came~~ caught ~~drank~~ drove ~~gave~~ ~~made~~
rang read said saw ~~sat~~ ~~went~~ wrote

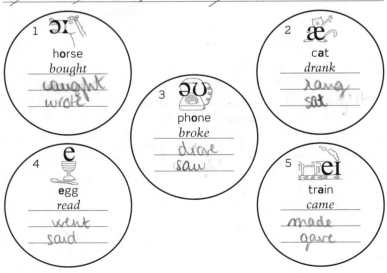

1 **or** horse
bought
caught
wrote

2 **æ** cat
drank
rang
sat

3 **əʊ** phone
broke
drove
saw

4 **e** egg
read
went
said

5 **eɪ** train
came
made
gave

d 🔊 2.2 Listen and check. Then listen again and repeat the words.

4 LISTENING

🔊 2.3 Listen to five speakers talking about holidays they didn't enjoy. Which speaker...?

a didn't have a very exciting weekend ___
b wasn't with the people he / she wanted to be with ___ 1
c chose a holiday destination because of the weather there ___
d went on holiday after a relationship ended ___
e didn't feel well when he / she was on holiday ___

~~Speaker 1~~   Speaker 2   Speaker 3

Speaker 4   Speaker 5

USEFUL WORDS AND PHRASES

Learn these words and phrases.

atmosphere /ˈætməsfɪə/
disaster /dɪˈzɑːstə/
hostels /ˈhɒstlz/
complain /kəmˈpleɪn/
enjoy /ɪnˈdʒɔɪ/
flirt /flɜːt/
view /vjuː/
break up /ˈbreɪk ʌp/
feel sorry for (sb) /fiːl ˈsɒri fɔː/
go wrong /gəʊ rɒŋ/

Photographs are pictures taken to please
the family and bore the neighbours.
Edmund Volkart, American sociologist

2B The story behind the photo

1 GRAMMAR past continuous

a Complete the sentences with the verbs in brackets in the past continuous.

1 You ___were laughing___ (laugh) when I took the photo.
2 It _was snowing_ (snow) when our plane landed.
3 We _weren't driving_ (not drive) fast when the accident happened.
4 What _he was doing_ (he / do) when his boss arrived?
5 Why _were you crying_ (you / cry) at the party?
6 I _was sitting_ (sit) on the bus when I saw my boyfriend with another girl.
7 They _were living_ (live) in New Zealand when their first child was born.
8 He didn't call you because his mobile phone _wasn't working_ (not work).

b Write sentences with *when*. Use the past simple and past continuous.

1 They / argue / the waiter / bring / the bill.
They were arguing when the waiter brought the bill .

2 He / fall / off his bike / cycle / home
He fell of his bike when he was cycling home.

3 The children / play / video games / the visitors / arrive
The children were playing when visitors arrived

4 We / have / a barbecue / it / start / to rain
We were having whe he stared .

5 I / finish / my report / my computer / crash
I was finishing when crashed .

c Complete the story with the past simple or past continuous.

Last summer I [1] ___went___ (go) to Los Angeles to stay with my cousin for a few weeks. One afternoon we [2] _we having_ (have) lunch in a nice restaurant in the centre of town when my cousin [3] ___got___ (get) a call on her mobile phone and went outside to talk. While she [4] _was speaking_ (speak) to her friend, I suddenly [5] _____ (notice) a man in a black hat who [6] _____ (sit) at the next table. It was the actor Johnny Depp! He was alone, and I [7] _____ (decide) to take my chance. So I got up and [8] ___went___ (go) to his table. 'Excuse me, could I have my photo taken with you?' I asked. He [9] _____ (say) yes, so I [10] _____ (stop) a waitress who [11] _____ (pass) by and gave her my camera. She [12] _____ (take) the photo of me and Johnny, I thanked them both, and then I returned to my table. When my cousin [13] _____ (come) back, I [14] _____ (smile).

'Why are you looking so pleased with yourself?' she asked.

'I had my photo taken with Johnny Depp.'

'Johnny Depp? Where is he?'

'He's sitting over there. Look!'

She turned around to look and then started to laugh.

'That's not Johnny Depp!'

I [15] _____ (look) at the man in the black hat – he [16] _____ (laugh) too.

2 VOCABULARY *at, in, on*

time

a Complete the sentences with *at*, *in*, or *on*.

1 The results of the election were announced __at__ 11 o'clock.
2 Mobile phones were invented _____ the 20th century.
3 Our flight is leaving _____ Wednesday at 9.30 _____ the evening and arriving _____ 12 o'clock _____ Thursday.
4 We have an exam _____ Monday morning.
5 In most countries, banks and offices are closed _____ Christmas Day and New Year's Day.
6 I hate driving _____ night, getting up early _____ the morning, and working _____ weekends.
7 Steve Jobs was born _____ 1955, and he died _____ 5th October, 2011.
8 _____ Easter we went to Portugal and we're going again _____ the summer, probably the last two weeks _____ July.

place

b Complete the sentences with *at*, *in*, or *on*.

1 He took some great photos __at__ the party.
2 I can't read a book _____ the bus or _____ a car.
3 We want to put some shelves _____ the wall _____ the living room. We're going to put all our old books _____ the shelves.
4 My family are from Ireland but we live _____ New York, _____ the 11th floor of a tall building.
5 I'll meet you _____ the bus stop.
6 The adults sat _____ chairs and the children sat _____ the floor.
7 They spent the morning _____ the museum and then went for a walk _____ the park.
8 I met my boyfriend _____ school and we split up while we were _____ university.

3 PRONUNCIATION sentence stress

2.4 Listen and repeat the dialogue. Copy the rhythm.

A **Where** were **you** at **ten** o'**clock** last **night**?
B I was at **home**.
A **What** were you **doing**?
B I was **watching** a **film**.

4 LISTENING

a 2.5 Listen to a conversation between Matt and Jenny about a photo. Does Jenny like the photo? _____

b Listen again and choose the best answers.

1 The photo shows…
   a Matt's parents.
   b Matt's aunt and uncle.
   c Matt's grandparents.
2 The photo was taken…
   a in the spring.
   b in the summer.
   c in the autumn.
3 The man wanted to win…
   a some money.
   b some food.
   c some jewellery.
4 The other people in the photo were the man's…
   a neighbours.
   b friends.
   c colleagues.
5 The man on the stall…
   a took the photo.
   b asked for more money for the photo.
   c didn't like the photo.

USEFUL WORDS AND PHRASES

Learn these words and phrases.

democracy /dɪˈmɒkrəsi/
demonstration /demənˈstreɪʃn/
election /ɪˈlekʃn/
freedom /ˈfriːdəm/
hold hands /həʊld hændz/
peace /piːs/
realize /ˈrɪəlaɪz/
TV screens /tiː ˈviː skriːnz/
upload /ʌpˈləʊd/
screen saver /skriːn ˈseɪvə/

2C One dark October evening

1 GRAMMAR time sequencers and connectors

a Circle the correct words or phrases.

[1] **The summer** /(**One summer**), I decided to travel to Peru. I flew to Lima, and then travelled to a town near Machu Picchu to spend the night. [2] **Next day** / **Afterday**, I climbed the mountain to visit the monument. I was quite tired [3] **when** / **then** I reached the top. [4] **Sudden** / **Suddenly**, I saw a man who was in my English class back home. [5] **Two minutes later** / **Two minutes after**, he came over to speak to me and he was just as surprised as I was. [6] **After that** / **When**, we decided to travel together. We had a great summer, and we carried on seeing each other back home. In fact, we got married two years later, and we now have a beautiful daughter called Hannah.

b Look at each group of sentences. Complete each sentence with *so*, *because*, *but*, or *although*.

1. a Linda ran to the station ___because___ she was very late.
   b Linda was very late ___so___ she ran to the station.
   c ___Although___ Linda ran to the station, she was too late and she missed the train.
2. a ___Because___ / ~~Although~~ we couldn't go out, we had a really good afternoon at home.
   b It was raining ___so___ we stayed at home.
   c We stayed at home last Sunday ___because___ it was raining.
3. a The tickets were really expensive ___but___ they managed to sell them all in an hour.
   b ___Although___ the tickets were really expensive, they sold them all in an hour.
   c They sold the tickets quickly ___because___ the concert was very popular.

c Rewrite the sentences using the words in brackets.

1. I didn't have any breakfast because I didn't have time. **(so)**
   I didn't have time ___so I didn't have any breakfast___.
2. I had a great holiday in Egypt although I can't speak Arabic. **(but)**
   I can't speak Arabic ___but I had a great holiday in Egypt___.
3. I don't really like Ryan, but I went on a date with him. **(although)**
   I went on a date with Ryan, ___although I don't really like him___.
4. I called the police because the door to my flat was open. **(so)**
   The door to my flat was open ___so I called the police___.
5. Jim has a lot of money, but he's really mean. **(although)**
   Jim's really mean, ___although he has a lot of money___.
6. Mary couldn't find her wallet so she cancelled her credit cards. **(because)**
   Mary cancelled her credit cards ___because she couldn't find her wallet___.

2 VOCABULARY verb phrases

a Match the phrases.

1. Jamie and Hannah met | [d] | a ~~her to dinner.~~
2. He played | [g] | b ~~for her at the door.~~
3. She left | [f] | c ~~a wonderful evening.~~
4. He waited | [b] | d ~~in a club.~~
5. She gave | [h] | e ~~to a new restaurant.~~
6. He invited | [a] | f ~~the club very late.~~
7. He took her | [e] | g ~~her favourite song.~~
8. They had | [c] | h ~~him her phone number.~~

b Cover the right-hand column. Try to remember the sentences.

3 PRONUNCIATION word stress

a Write the words in the chart.

~~across~~ after ~~again~~ although ~~awful~~ because ~~birthday~~
evening invite perfect restaurant second

1 First syllable stressed	2 Second syllable stressed
after	*across*
birthday	invite
perfect	because
evening	again
restaurant	although
awful	
second	

b 🔊 2.6 Listen and check. Then listen again and repeat the words.

4 READING

a Read the story. Number the paragraphs in the right order.

A lucky escape

☐ Ten minutes later, it began to rain. Soon, Liz found it hard to see out of the front windscreen. There was a lot of water on the road, so she drove more slowly. Although Liz was an experienced driver, she felt afraid.

☐ An hour later, fire fighters cut Liz out of the car. She went to hospital, but the doctors sent her home because she didn't have any serious injuries. Her head was fine and she only had a few cuts and bruises. Her son went to collect the shopping from the car and gave the loaf of bread to his mum. Now, she is going to keep it as a souvenir.

1 One day last November, Liz Douglas decided to go shopping in Glasgow. She drove to the supermarket in the city centre and spent the morning doing her weekly shop. She paid for her shopping, went back to the car park, and put the shopping bags on the back seat of the car. Then she started to drive home.

☐ However, Liz was lucky. When she braked, a loaf of bread flew out of one of the shopping bags. The car turned over, and the loaf of bread landed between Liz's head and the roof of the car. It stopped her head from hitting the car roof.

☐ Suddenly, she lost control of the car. She saw a telegraph pole in front of her and braked. She closed her eyes and hoped that the airbags in the car would inflate. Unfortunately, they didn't.

b Look at the highlighted words. What do you think they mean? Check with your dictionary.

5 LISTENING

🔊 2.7 Listen to a radio programme about people who had lucky escapes. Mark the sentences T (true) or F (false).

1 Maureen Evason was on holiday when the accident happened. _T_
2 She was in hospital for four months. __
3 Joseph Rabadue was sitting on the floor when the accident happened. __
4 The lorry hit the TV. __
5 Barry McRoy was drinking coffee when the fight happened. __
6 The DVD was in his jacket pocket. __

USEFUL WORDS AND PHRASES

Learn these words and phrases.

anniversary /ˌænɪˈvɜːsəri/
brake /breɪk/
perfect /ˈpɜːfɪkt/
as usual /əz ˈjuːʒəl/
cross the road /krɒs ðə rəʊd/
High Street /ˈhaɪ striːt/
happy ending /ˈhæpi ˈendɪŋ/
just in time /dʒʌst ɪn ˈtaɪm/
madly in love /ˈmædli ɪn lʌv/
until the last moment /ənˈtɪl ðə lɑːst ˈməʊmənt/

I'd like to fly. Then I wouldn't have to wait in airport security lines.

Jim Morris, American baseball player

3A Plans and dreams

1 GRAMMAR *be going to* (plans and predictions)

a Complete the sentences with *going to* + a verb from the box.

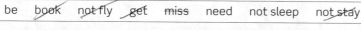

be   book   not fly   get   miss   need   not sleep   not stay

1 He's __*going to miss*__ the flight.

2 I going to book my flight online.

3 He's going during the flight.

4 How is she _____ to the airport?

5 That plane is not going to fly today.

6 They _____ late.

7 I _____ in a hotel.

8 Are we going to need a trolley?

b Complete the dialogue with *going to* + the verbs.

Jenny ¹ __*Are you going to have*__ (you/have) a holiday this summer?

Philip Yes, but ² _____ (we / not / go) to the Mediterranean. ³ _____ (we / go) to Scotland!

Jenny When ⁴ *are you going to* travel (you / travel)?

Philip In August. ⁵ _____ (we / be) there for two weeks.

Jenny What ⁶ _____ (you / do) while you're there?

Philip ⁷ _____ (we / stay) in Edinburgh for a week, and then ⁸ _____ (we / rent) a car and visit the Scottish Highlands.

Jenny ⁹ _____ (it / be) sunny in Scotland in August?

Philip I don't know. But I hope ¹⁰ _____ (it / not / rain) too much!

2 VOCABULARY airports

Complete the text.

Last summer, I flew to New York with my boyfriend to visit some friends. The flight left from ¹Terminal 1, so my brother dropped us outside the building. We went inside and looked for the ²lift _____ to take us upstairs to ³Departures _____. We picked up our boarding passes at the ⁴ch_____. Then we did some shopping. After that, we made our way to the ⁵g_____ to board our plane. We had a good flight, but we were very tired when we landed at JFK Airport. There was a long·queue at ⁶p_____ c_____, and they asked us a lot of questions at Immigration. Finally, we went to ⁷B_____ R_____ to pick up our bags. We needed a ⁸trolley _____ this time because of all our suitcases. Nobody stopped us at ⁹Customes _____, so we went straight to ¹⁰Arrivals _____, where our friends were waiting for us.

17

3 PRONUNCIATION sentence stress and fast speech

3.1 Listen and repeat. <u>Copy</u> the <u>rhy</u>thm.

1 **Are** they **going** to **meet** you at the **airport**?
2 I **think** we're **going** to be **late**.
3 I'm **not going** to **forget** my **passport**.
4 **What time** are you **going** to **arrive**?
5 She's **going** to **take** the **lift**.

4 READING

a Read the text. How many airports is Beijing going to have in 2020? ___4___

b Read the text again. Mark the sentences T (true) or F (false).

1 More than 54 million people use Atlanta International Airport each year. _F_
2 Atlanta International isn't going to be the busiest airport in 2020. _F_
3 A new airport was built for the 2008 Olympic Games. _F_
4 Beijing Capital Airport is too small. _T_
5 In the future, Beijing's Metro is going to reach the new airport. _T_
6 The new airport is going to have eight runways. _T/F_

c Look at the highlighted words. What do you think they mean? Check with your dictionary.

5 LISTENING

a **3.2** Listen to five conversations at the airport. Match the speakers with the places in the box.

~~Arrivals~~	Baggage reclaim	Check-in
Customs	Immigration	

Dialogue 1	_Arrivals_
Dialogue 2	_____
Dialogue 3	_____
Dialogue 4	_____
Dialogue 5	_____

b Listen again and answer the questions.

1 What did the man eat on the plane?
2 What's the Gate number?
3 What's the friend's phone number?
4 What colour is the suitcase?
5 What did the woman buy?

The World's Biggest Airport

The world's busiest airport today is in the USA. Nearly 54 million passengers pass through Atlanta International Airport every year. However, by the end of the next decade there's going to be a new airport even bigger and busier than Atlanta. The new airport is going to be in the capital of China: Beijing.

Beijing already has two airports. The first is Beijing Capital, where an extra terminal was built for the 2008 Olympic Games. The second is Nanyuan Airport, which is mainly used by military planes . Just over 37 million passengers passed through Beijing Capital Airport last year, making it the second busiest after Atlanta. But the current airport is not big enough for all the Chinese passengers who want to travel by plane. This is why the government is going to build a new one.

The new airport is going to be in the suburb of Daxing, in the south of the city. Daxing is about an hour's drive from the city centre. The government is going to extend Beijing's Metro so that passengers can reach it more easily. There are also plans for a high-speed train line. The airport is going to have eight runways for commercial flights, and a ninth runway for military use. This is going to make it the biggest and the busiest airport in the world.

USEFUL WORDS AND PHRASES

Learn these words and phrases.

dreams /driːmz/
facilities /fəˈsɪlətiz/
paradise /ˈpærədaɪs/
passenger /ˈpæsɪndʒə/
security /sɪˈkjʊərəti/
traveller /ˈtrævələ/

board /bɔːd/
delayed /dɪˈleɪd/
free (Wi-fi) /friː/
connecting flight / kəˈnektɪŋ flaɪt/

The future belongs to those who believe
in the beauty of their dreams.

Eleanor Roosevelt

3B Let's meet again

1 GRAMMAR present continuous (future arrangements)

a Complete the text with the present continuous form of the verbs in brackets.

'Hi, I'm Lisa, your guide, and I'm going to tell you about the arrangements for your day trip to Paris. We [1] *'re starting* (start) our trip in about five minutes, so please make yourselves comfortable. We [2] *'re driving* (drive) you straight to Dover – we [3] *'re not stoping* (not stop) for breakfast on the way. We [4] *'re getting* (get) the 9.15 ferry, so we're in a bit of a hurry. When we arrive in France, we [5] *'re going* (go) straight to Paris with no stops. We [6] *'re not taking* (not take) you to the city centre, because the traffic is terrible. We [7] *'re stoping* (stop) in Torcy, just outside Paris. We [8] *'re arriving* (arrive) in Paris at about midday, so you have all afternoon to go sightseeing and shop. We [9] *'re picking* (pick) you up from the station in Torcy at 5.30 in the evening. We [10] *'re catching* (catch) the ferry home at 8.45, so please don't be late. Now, any questions?'

b Circle the correct verb form. If both forms are possible, tick (✓) the sentence.

1 **A** Why are you looking so worried?
  B I'm sure **I'm going to get** / I'm getting lost.

2 **A** Do you have any plans for this weekend?
  B Yes, **I'm going to visit** / **I'm visiting** my grandparents on Sunday. ✓

3 **A** I'm going to Poland next week.
  B Really? Do you think **it's going to be** / it's being cold?

4 **A** My brother has a job interview in London.
  B Oh. Do you think **he's going to get** / he's getting the job?

5 **A** What time's the train?
  B At 7.15. Don't worry. We **aren't going to miss** / aren't missing it.

6 **A** We're going on holiday next month.
  B Are you? Where **are you going to go** / **are you going**?

7 **A** How do you get to work?
  B I usually catch the bus, but tomorrow **I'm going to drive** / **I'm driving** because the buses are on strike. ✓

8 **A** Your girlfriend drives too fast.
  B I know. I'm sure **she's going to have** / she's having an accident one day.

2 VOCABULARY verbs + prepositions

Complete the sentences with the correct prepositions.

1 I completely agree ___with___ you.
2 We're arriving ___in___ Brazil at 6 a.m.
3 I'm worried ___about___ my flight because it's snowing.
4 They're waiting ___for___ Anna. She's late.
5 She spends a lot of money ___on___ clothes.
6 I want to speak ___with___ my boss after lunch.
7 Sarah's arriving ___at___ the airport tonight.
8 What do you think ___about___ the government's proposal?

3 PRONUNCIATION sounding friendly

a Number the dialogue in the correct order.

_1_ Would you like to go away for the weekend?
_2_ What about next weekend? What are you doing then?
_3_ Are you free this weekend?
_8_ I love it!
_5_ OK. Let's go to Devon – the countryside is beautiful!
_2_ Sorry, no. I'm working on Saturday.
_5_ Nothing. Next weekend is fine.
_X_ I'd love to.
_7_ Great. Do you like walking?

b 🔊 **3.3** Listen and check. Then listen again and repeat the sentences. Copy the rhythm.

4 READING

a Read the advert for a holiday. How many nights does the tour last?

Tour of the Magic Triangle: Prague – Vienna – Budapest

Visit these three beautiful capital cities and discover their historic monuments and lively atmosphere. Enjoy three wonderful cultural performances and return with unforgettable memories.

Prague

The tour starts in Prague, capital of the Czech Republic. A free bus takes you from the airport to your hotel, where you spend three nights. The price includes a tour of the city, a cruise on the Vltava River, a visit to a spa resort, and a performance at the Laterna Magika theatre. From Prague you travel first class by train to your next destination: Vienna.

Vienna

The Austrian capital has many spectacular monuments, which you can visit with the free 72-hour travel card which you receive when you arrive in Vienna. The price also includes a tour of the city, Viennese coffee and cakes at the famous Hotel Sacher, and a performance at the opera. After your three nights in Vienna you travel first class by train to your final destination: Budapest.

Budapest

You spend your last three nights in Budapest, the capital city of Hungary, where there are plenty of places to explore. The city is divided into two parts: the old historic city of Buda on the hill, and the commercial city of Pest on the other side of the River Danube. The price includes a tour of the city with a visit to the Parliament building, a typical Hungarian dinner, a performance of classical music, and the return journey from your hotel to the airport.

At only €1599, this is an opportunity you cannot afford to miss!

b Read the advert again. Answer the questions with P (Prague), V (Vienna), or B (Budapest).

In which city do customers…?
1 travel free on public transport   _V_
2 have a traditional evening meal   _B_
3 go on a boat trip   _P_
4 listen to a concert   _V_
5 have a drink and sweet snack   _V_
6 go to a place to relax   _P_

c <u>Underline</u> five words you don't know. Use your dictionary to look up their meaning and pronunciation.

5 LISTENING

a ◖ 3.4 Listen to two people, Chris and Dawn, talking about an Interrailing holiday. Which countries is Dawn visiting?

b Listen again and correct the sentences.
1 Dawn is going Interrailing **on her own**.
    with a friend
2 Chris went Interrailing when he was **a child**.
3 Dawn is going Interrailing for **a month**.
4 Dawn's first stop in Italy is **Milan**.
5 Dawn wants to visit **the Eiffel Tower** in Paris.
6 Dawn is spending most nights **on the train**.

USEFUL WORDS AND PHRASES

Learn these words and phrases.

(travel) arrangements /əˈreɪndʒmənts/	still /stɪl/
conference /ˈkɒnfərəns/	both of us /ˈbəʊθ əv ʌs/
news /njuːz/	I'd love to /aɪd ˈlʌv tuː/
fix /fɪks/	for ages /fə(r) ˈeɪdʒɪz/
perhaps /pəˈhæps/	How are things? /haʊ ə ˈθɪŋz/

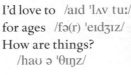

What is a rebel? A man who says no.

Albert Camus, French writer

3C What's the word?

1 GRAMMAR defining relative clauses

a Match the beginnings and ends of the sentences.

1 That's the hotel   f
2 I need a phone   a
3 My mum is the only person   d
4 I love the picture   h
5 That bus is the one   b
6 Benicassim is the Spanish town   g
7 David Hockney is the artist   e
8 That's the restaurant   c

a which has a good camera.
b which my brother takes to work.
c which serves fresh fish.
d who remembers my birthday.
e who painted *Mr & Mrs Clarke*.
f where we spent our honeymoon.
g where they have a famous music festival.
h which is on the wall of your room.

b Complete the sentences with *who*, *which*, or *where*.

1 Do you know the man __who__ lives next door?
2 That's the gallery __where__ had the Leonardo da Vinci exhibition.
3 Are those the people __who__ are selling their house?
4 Do you know a good restaurant ~~which~~ which is open on Sunday night?
5 Is that the bus __which__ goes to the airport?
6 We walked past the school __where__ their children go.
7 She's the woman __who__ everyone is talking about.
8 I took my laptop back to the shop __where__ I bought it.
9 Antwerp is the city __where__ I lived as a child.
10 Is there someone __who__ can speak Arabic in your class?

2 VOCABULARY expressions for paraphrasing: *like, for example*, etc.

Complete the sentences for explaining words.

1 *mean*   It's the o__pposite__ of generous.
2 *cardigan* It's a k_____ of jumper.
3 *hire*   It's s__omething__ to *rent*.
4 *slim*   It's l_____ *thin*, but it's more polite.
5 *souvenir* It's s__omething__ you buy to remind you of your holiday.
6 *sunbathe* For e__xample__, you do this on the beach.
7 *pilot*   It's s__omeone__ who flies a plane.
8 *campsite* It's s__omewhere__ you can sleep in tents.

3 PRONUNCIATION pronunciation in a dictionary

a Match the words with their pronunciation. Use your dictionary.

1 beard   *b*   a /bɔːld/
   bald   *a*   b /bɪəd/

2 quiet   b   a /kwaɪt/
   quite   a   b /ˈkwaɪət/

3 shoes   a   a /ʃuːz/
   socks   b   b /sɒks/

4 suit   b   a /swiːt/
   sweet   a   b /suːt/

5 sightsee   a   a /ˈsaɪtsiː/
   sunbathe   b   b /ˈsʌnbeɪð/

6 height   b   a /weɪt/
   weight   a   b /haɪt/

7 shirt   a   a /ʃɜːt/
   shorts   b   b /ʃɔːts/

8 crowded   b   a /ˈklaʊdi/
   cloudy   a   b /ˈkraʊdɪd/

b ◐ 3.5 Listen and check. Then listen again and repeat the words.

4 READING

a Read the definitions and complete them with these words.

agritourism   chick lit   E-waste   fashionista   netiquette   sandwich generation   staycation   web rage

More new words in English

1   _Web rage_ is the angry feeling you get because of a problem with the internet.

2   A _fashionista_ is a person who always wears the latest styles.

3   _chick lit_ is a kind of book which tells a story from a woman's point of view.

4   _E-waste_ is all the electrical machines and devices which people throw away.

5   The _sandwich generation_ is a group of people who look after their parents at the same time as they're looking after their children.

6   _Agritourism_ is a kind of holiday where people stay on farms and help with all the work.

7   _Netiquette_ is a set of rules which explains how to be polite on the internet.

8   A _staycation_ is a holiday which you spend at home.

b <u>Underline</u> five more words you don't know. Use your dictionary to look up their meaning and pronunciation.

5 LISTENING

a 🔊 3.6 Listen to a radio programme about the word game *Scrabble*. How many different names has the game had?

b Listen again. Mark the sentences T (true) or F (false).

1   Alfred Mosher Butts was out of work when he invented the game.   _T_

2   The game of *Lexico* had a board and letter tiles.   —

3   Butts used a newspaper to count the frequency of the letters in English.   —

4   Butts gave the letters A, E, I, O, and U one point each.   —

5   Butts gave 12 points to the most difficult letters to use.   —

6   *Scrabble* became popular in 1948.   —

7   Butts and Brunot sold the game to another manufacturer.   —

8   You can buy *Scrabble* in more than a hundred different countries.   —

USEFUL WORDS AND PHRASES

Learn these words and phrases.

barista /bəˈrɪstə/
gastropub /ˈgæstrəʊpʌb/
latte /ˈlɑːteɪ/
smartphone /ˈsmɑːtfəʊn/
google /ˈguːgl/
text /tekst/
tweet /twiːt/
update /ˈʌpdeɪt/
road rage /rəʊd reɪdʒ/
toy boy /ˈtɔɪbɔɪ/

Practical English Restaurant problems

1 VOCABULARY

Complete the sentences.

1 Can we have a t_able__ for two, please?
2 What's on the m_enu_____ today?
3 The st_art_____ is chicken soup or tomato salad.
4 I'll have the steak for my m_ain____ _course___.
5 Let's ask the w_aitress/er____ for another bottle of water.
6 I don't want a d_essert____, but I'd like a coffee.
7 Can we have the b_ill_____, please?

2 AT THE RESTAURANT

Order the dialogue.

A	Are you ready to order?	_1_
B	Still.	_12_
A	Still or sparkling?	_11_
B	Yes, please.	_2_
A	And how would you like your steak? Rare, medium or well done?	_5_
B	A baked potato, please.	_8_
A	Can I get you something to start with?	_3_
B	Rare, please.	_6_
A	Here's your steak, madam.	_13_
B	Water, please.	_10_
A	Would you like that with fries or with a baked potato?	_7_
B	I'm sorry but I asked for my steak rare and this is well done.	_14_
A	OK. And to drink?	_9_
B	No, thank you. Just a main course. I'd like the steak, please.	_4_
A	I'm very sorry, madam. I'll take it back to the kitchen.	_15_

3 SOCIAL ENGLISH

Complete the sentences with the words in the box.

a mistake   any suggestions   be great   my day
start with   tell me   to go   we have

1 A So, __tell me__, Adam, what are your plans?
  B Well, to _start with_, I'd like to see the world.
2 A I'd like to go sightseeing this afternoon. Do you have _any suggestions_?
  B How about going to Central Park? I could take you.
  A That would _be great_.
3 A Could _we have_ the check, please?
  B Yes of course. Here you are.
4 A Excuse me. I think there's _a mistake_.
  B Oh, sorry. It's not _my day_ today.
5 A It's very late.
  B Yes. Time _to go_.

4 READING

a Read the article and answer the questions.

1 How many restaurants are there in new York? _Over 20,000_
2 What time do restaurants serve Early Bird menus?
   They serve at 5 pm to 7 pm.
3 How much is the Early Bird menu at Cucina di Pesce?
   It costs $12.95
4 Where is La Paella? _214 E 9th St_
5 Which restaurants serve a Pre-Theatre Dinner Menu? _strict_
   It costs $12.85 The Theatre Dinner
6 How much do they cost? _Between $30 and $45_
7 When is it cheapest to eat in a four-star restaurant?
   In the Jean Georges At lunch time
8 What kind of food can you eat at Aquavit?
   Scandinavian Food.

Eating out in NY

New York City has over 20,000 restaurants serving all kinds of food. However, eating out in the Big Apple can be very expensive. Here are some tips on how to save money during your stay.

Early Bird Menus

These are meals served in some New York restaurants between 5 p.m. and 7 p.m., when they would normally be empty. If you don't mind having dinner early, you can enjoy a three-course meal for between $13 and $25.

Cucina di Pesce (87 E.4th St) serves great Italian food on its $12.95 Early Bird menu. If you prefer something Spanish, you can try the $16.99 Early Bird menu at **La Paella** (214 E.9th St).

Pre-Theatre Dinner Menus

These are similar to Early Bird Menus, but they are served in the Theatre District. Most of the restaurants here offer a set menu at a fixed price ranging from $30 to $45. The offer is only available before the show, and it starts at 5 p.m.

Four-Star Restaurants

These are all very expensive at dinnertime, so why not have lunch there instead? That way you can get dinner quality food at lunchtime menu prices. **Aquavit** (65 E.55th St) serves fantastic Scandinavian food on a great lunch menu and **Jean Georges** (1 Central Park West) offers an excellent two-course lunch for only $28.

b Underline five words or phrases you don't know. Use your dictionary to look up their meaning and pronunciation.

Few things are more satisfying than seeing your children have teenagers of their own.

Doug Larson, American journalist

4A Parents and teenagers

1 VOCABULARY housework, *make* or *do*?

a Complete the expressions with the verbs in the box.

clean	do	lay	make	~~pick up~~	put away	tidy	take out

1 *pick up* _____ dirty clothes
2 _____ the beds, lunch
3 _____ your room, your desk
4 _____ the table for dinner
5 _____ the floor, the bathroom
6 _____ the rubbish, the newspapers
7 _____ the ironing, the washing up
8 _____ the clothes on your bed

b Complete the sentences with *do* or *make*.

1 He never forgets to __*do*__ his homework after school.
2 I try not to _____ a noise when I get up early.
3 My husband doesn't often _____ lunch.
4 I'm going to _____ a course in Portuguese before I go to Brazil.
5 We always _____ housework on Saturday morning.
6 Some children _____ friends easily when they go to school.
7 When do you have time to _____ sport?
8 Sorry, I need to _____ a phone call.

2 GRAMMAR present perfect + *yet*, *just*, *already*

a Add *already* or *yet* to these sentences in the correct place.

1 I've done the washing.
   I've already done the washing _____ .
2 Have you made any plans for the weekend?
   _____ ?
3 We haven't finished lunch.
   _____ .
4 Daniel has tidied his room.
   _____ .
5 I've done the ironing.
   _____ .
6 Have you been to the supermarket?
   _____ ?
7 I haven't cleaned the bathroom.
   _____ .
8 Edward has taken out the rubbish.
   _____ .

b Complete the sentences for each picture. Use *just* + present perfect and a verb from the list.

clean	~~do~~	lay	win	miss	fall

1 She*'s just done* _____ the washing up.
2 He _____ off his bike.
3 They _____ the championship.
4 'I _____ the floor.'
5 He _____ the table.
6 'Sorry. You _____ dinner.'

3 PRONUNCIATION /j/, /dʒ/

a Write a word containing the sound in the pictures.

1 a person at university __*student*__
2 the opposite of *old* _____
3 twelve months _____
4 a colour _____
5 special clothes for school _____

6 a kind of short coat _____
7 a person between 13 and 19 years old _____
8 something that crosses a river _____
9 another word for *sweater* _____
10 get pleasure from something _____

b ◖4.1 Listen and check. Then listen again and repeat the words.

4 READING

a Read the text. Which is the best title?

1 **Having a cleaner house**
2 **Equality in the home**
3 **Improving your relationship**

Men and women all over the world have arguments about doing the housework, and it's usually the women who lose. However, a recent study by researchers at Oxford University shows that the situation is slowly improving.

The researchers asked men and women aged between 20 and 59 to keep a diary of how much time they spent on housework each day. Then the researchers collected the diaries and analyzed them.

These showed that women in the UK today spend about four hours and 40 minutes each day doing housework. Men, on the other hand, spend two hours and 28 minutes doing the same things. Although women still spend more time doing domestic jobs, the figures show that the situation has improved. In the 1960s, women spent six hours a day on housework and men only 90 minutes.

Researchers say that women are still doing most of the housework because people still divide domestic jobs into two areas. They see cooking, cleaning, and looking after children as 'women's work', and general repairs, car maintenance , and work outside the home as 'men's work'.

So, in general, the results of the study bring good news for women. The difference between the amount of time men and women spend on housework is getting smaller every year. This means that the time will come when both sexes share domestic chores equally. However, women will have to be extremely patient, because the change won't be complete for another four decades!

b Read the text. Mark the sentences T (true) or F (false).

1 Men and women don't always agree about housework.   _T_

2 Adults and teenagers took part in the study.   ___

3 The participants had to write down the time they spent on housework.   ___

4 The time people spend doing housework has changed since the 1960s.   ___

5 Today, women do more housework than they did in the 1960s.   ___

6 In general, people think it's normal for women to look after the family car.   ___

7 Forty years from now, men and women will share the housework.   ___

c Look at the highlighted words. What do you think they mean? Use your dictionary to look up their meaning and pronunciation.

5 LISTENING

a 4.2 Listen to five teenagers talking about housework. Which speaker does the most housework?

_____

b Listen again. Match the speakers with what they say about housework.

Speaker 1   _B_   A We all share it.
Speaker 2   ___   B My mum does it all.
Speaker 3   ___   C We pay someone to do it.
Speaker 4   ___   D There's one thing I like doing.
Speaker 5   ___   E I do a little every day.

USEFUL WORDS AND PHRASES

Learn these words and phrases.

carer /ˈkeərə/
plate /pleɪt/
reputation /repjuˈteɪʃn/
teenager /ˈtiːneɪdʒə/
wardrobe /ˈwɔːdrəʊb/
dry (your hair) /draɪ/
knock (on the door) /nɒk/
carry on (texting) /ˈkæri ɒn/
switch off (your mobile) /swɪtʃ ɒf/
TV channel /tiːviː ˈtʃænl/

4B Fashion and shopping

1 VOCABULARY shopping

a Complete the text.

SHOPPING IN A SHOP OR STORE

I usually go shopping in my lunch break, so I don't have time to ¹t*ry* on clothes. There's always a long queue for the ²ch_____ r_____, so I just take them straight to the ³ch_____ to pay. I keep the ⁴r_____ so I can change them if they don't ⁵s_____ me. Sometimes I get the wrong ⁶s_____, and the clothes don't ⁷f_____. I often ⁸t_____ things b_____ to shops, but the ⁹sh_____ a_____ don't seem to mind at all.

b Complete the crossword.

				¹A
	²			C
³				C
				O
⁴	⁵			U
				N
	⁶			T
⁷				
⁸				

Shopping online

Clues down ↓

1 When you shop online, you normally have to create an a*ccount* which has your personal details.
2 Something you want to buy is called an it_____.
5 eBay is an online au_____ site, which sells things to the person who offers the most money.
7 Amazon is a popular w_____ where you can buy things such as books, computers, and clothes.

Clues across →

3 When you find something you want to buy on a website, you put it in your shopping b_____.
4 You can make a p_____ in different ways, e.g. using your credit card or Paypal.
6 When you are ready to buy something, you go to the ch_____.
8 You have to enter your d_____ address so they can send your things to the correct place.

2 GRAMMAR present perfect or past simple?

a Write sentences and questions with the present perfect. Use contractions where possible.

1 she / buy / a new jacket ⊞
  She's bought a new jacket. .

2 I / bring / my / credit card ⊟
  _____ .

3 Anna / go shopping ❓
  _____ ?

4 your sister / ever work / as a model ❓
  _____ ?

5 you / wear / your new shirt ⊟
  _____ .

6 I / ever tell you/ about my holiday in Greece ❓
  _____ ?

7 the shopping centre / never be / so crowded ⊞
  _____ .

8 I / never use / eBay ⊞
  _____ .

b Complete the dialogues. Use the present perfect or past simple.

1 **A** _Have you ever bought_ (you / ever / buy) any clothes on the internet?
  B Yes, I _have_ .
  A What _did you buy_ (you / buy)?
  B I _bought_ (buy) a dress for a wedding, but it didn't fit!

2 **A** _____ (you / ever / sell) anything on eBay?
  B Yes, I _____.
  A What _____ (you / sell)?
  B Some CDs. I _____ (not want) them any more.

3 **A** _____ (you / ever / wear) any expensive jewellery?
  B No, I _____.

4 **A** _____ (you / ever / lose) your wallet?
  B Yes, I _____. I _____ (leave) it in a trolley at the supermarket.

5 **A** _____ (you / ever / have) an argument with a shop assistant?
  B Yes, I _____. I _____ (not have) the receipt, so I _____ (not can) change some boots.

3 PRONUNCIATION c and ch

a ◗ 4.3 Listen and circle the word with a different sound.

k key	1	customer account (choose)
k key	2	click proceed chemist's
s snake	3	clothes city centre
s snake	4	receive card cinema

b Listen again and repeat the words.

4 LISTENING

a ◗ 4.4 Listen to a news story. What is Westfield?
  _____ .

b Listen again and answer the questions.

1 How long has it taken to build Westfield?
  Six years .

2 How much did the shopping centre cost?
  _____ .

3 How many department stores and shops are there?
  _____ .

4 How many cafés and restaurants are there?
  _____ .

5 How many people work at Westfield?
  _____ .

6 How can you get to Westfield?
  _____ .

7 What did the reporter want to buy?
  _____ .

8 Why didn't the reporter buy the thing she liked?
  _____ .

USEFUL WORDS AND PHRASES

Learn these words and phrases.

bride /braɪd/
bridegroom
  /'braɪdgruːm/
leather /'leðə/
sew /səʊ/
bare feet /beə fiːt/
fancy dress /fænsi 'dres/

fashion designer
  /'fæʃn dɪzaɪnə/
high heels /'haɪ hiːlz/
wedding dress
  /'wedɪŋ dres/
take off (your shoes)
  /teɪk ɒf/

27

4C Lost weekend

1 GRAMMAR *something, anything, nothing, etc.*

a Circle the correct word.

1 We didn't do **anything** / **nothing** special last weekend.
2 Do you know **anything** / **anyone** about the meeting today?
3 There isn't **anywhere** / **nowhere** to go in the evenings.
4 He couldn't find his keys **nowhere** / **anywhere**.
5 We didn't know **someone** / **anyone** at the party.
6 Daniel has **something** / **anything** to tell you.
7 I phoned twice, but **anybody** / **nobody** answered.
8 We need to find **somewhere** / **anywhere** to stay in Dublin.
9 Listen! I think **somebody** / **anybody** is upstairs.

b Look at the picture. Mark the sentences T (true) or F (false).

1 There isn't anywhere to sit.   F
2 The man on the right is eating something.   T
3 Nobody is dancing.   T
4 There's nothing on the ground.   F
5 Someone is playing with the dog.   T
6 The man cooking doesn't have anything on his head.   F
7 There isn't anybody in the swimming pool.   F

2 VOCABULARY adjectives ending *-ed* and *-ing*

Complete the sentences with an adjective ending *-ed* or *-ing*.

1 I'm reading a really in*teresting* book.
2 Going to a spa for the weekend is so r_____.
3 This film is really b_____. Turn the TV off.
4 Helen's very d_____. She's just lost her job.
5 My cousin is very in_____ in archaeology.
6 Congratulations! That's really ex_____ news.
7 The news at the moment is all very d_____.
8 We always feel very r_____ on holiday.
9 Mum, I'm b_____! I have nothing to do!
10 The dogs were very ex_____ to see us when
    we came home.

3 PRONUNCIATION /e/, /əʊ/, /ʌ/

a 🔊 4.5 Listen and write the words in the chart.

> anything   ~~clever~~   ~~clothes~~   coat   ~~customer~~
> don't   dress   friendly   funny   gloves
> goes   home   lunch   nothing   photos
> something   sweater   website

1 ⊖ egg	2 ☎ phone	3 ↑ up
clever	*clothes*	*customer*
_____	_____	_____
_____	_____	_____
_____	_____	_____
_____	_____	_____

b Listen and check. Then listen again and repeat the words.

4 READING

a Complete the text with the activities.

Bake a loaf of bread   Play board games
Listen to some podcasts   Start a blog
Learn how to juggle   Take some photos
Meet your neighbours   Tidy your wardrobe
Organize your shelves   ~~Visit a library~~

Ten things to do during a money-free weekend

The weekend is the time when most people spend the most money. Here are some activities you can do if you want to save money.

1   _Visit a library_   It doesn't cost anything to borrow a book and there may be some DVDs you want to watch.

2   _____ Throw away any clothes you never wear, or give them to a charity.

3   _____ Many websites have interesting interviews you can listen to for free.

4   _____ This is a great way of spending time with the whole family.

5   _____ You probably have the ingredients in a cupboard – the result is delicious!

6   _____ All you need is three balls and a video showing you how to do it.

7   _____ Invite them over for a coffee and a chat and get to know them better.

8   _____ Decide which books, CDs, and DVDs you want to keep and get rid of the rest.

9   _____ Go for a walk with your digital camera. You'll be surprised at how beautiful your city is.

10   _____ Not only is it fun, but writing improves your communication skills.

b <u>Underline</u> five words you don't know. Use your dictionary to look up their meaning and pronunciation.

5 LISTENING

a 🔊 4.6 Listen to four people talking about their weekends. Where did they go?

Speaker 1   _____
Speaker 2   _____
Speaker 3   _____
Speaker 4   _____

b Listen again. Which speaker…?

1   cooked a meal   ___
2   played with children   ___
3   went to a different country   ___
4   saw some interesting exhibitions   ___
5   had an argument   _1_
6   woke up early   ___
7   had bad weather   _1_
8   gave someone a surprise   ___

USEFUL WORDS AND PHRASES

Learn these words and phrases.

survey /ˈsɜːveɪ/
encourage /ɪnˈkʌrɪdʒ/
impress /ɪmˈpres/
invent /ɪnˈvent/
lie (about sth) /laɪ/
lie down /laɪ ˈdaʊn/
do paperwork /də ˈpeɪpəwɜːk/
press (the button) /pres/
tell the truth /tel ðə ˈtruːθ/
lift button /ˈlɪft bʌtn/

Time is the coin of your life. Only you can decide how to spend it. Don't let other people spend it for you.

Carl Sandburg, American poet

5A No time for anything

1 GRAMMAR comparative adjectives and adverbs, *as...as...*

a Complete the sentences with the correct comparative form of the adjective / adverb.

1 My new boss is _*more patient*_ than the old one. (patient)
2 Pollution is _worst_ in cities than it is in the country. (bad)
3 We aren't in a hurry. You can drive _more slowly_. (slowly)
4 The summers here are _hotest / hotter_ than they were in the past. (hot)
5 I failed the test. I'll work _harder_ next time. (hard)
6 It's _further_ to my parents' house than it is to my boyfriend's. (far)
7 You can make the dinner tonight. You cook _better_ than me. (good)
8 The Japanese diet is _more healthy / healthier_ than the American diet. (healthy)
9 A motorbike is _more dangerous_ than a car. (dangerous)
10 Heathrow airport is _busiest / busier_ than Manchester airport. (busy)

b Rewrite the sentences using *as...as*.

1 This car goes faster than that one.
That car doesn't _go as fast as this one_.
2 Her shoes were more stylish than her handbag.
Her handbag wasn't _as stylish as her shoes_.
3 My boss's office is bigger than mine.
My office isn't _as bigger as_.
4 Spain played better than the Netherlands.
The Netherlands didn't _as play as well as Spain_.
5 I drive more carefully than you.
You don't _drive as carefull as me_.
6 Laptops are more expensive than mobile phones.
Mobile phones aren't _as expensive as laptops_.
7 Harry looks more relaxed than Sally.
Sally doesn't _looks as relax as Harry_.
8 His shirt was dirtier than his trousers.
His trousers weren't _as dirty as his shirt_.

2 VOCABULARY time expressions

Complete the sentences with the words in the box.

~~in~~	~~on~~	~~save~~	spend	~~take~~	waste

1 The flight to Beijing is going to _take_ about 11 hours.
2 She needs to _spend_ more time studying.
3 I hope we arrive _on_ time. My dad is meeting me at the airport.
4 Don't _waste_ time doing things you don't enjoy.
5 We'll _save_ time if we go on the motorway. There's much less traffic.
6 My girlfriend gets very stressed when she's _in_ a hurry.

3 PRONUNCIATION word stress

a Underline the stressed syllable in these words.

1 fa|ster
2 cen|tre
3 pa|rents
4 a|go
5 chil|dren
6 pa|tient
7 prob|lem
8 co|mmu|ni|ca|tion
9 tra|di|tio|nal
10 a|round
11 se|conds
12 be|tter

b Now circle the /ə/ sound.

1 fast(er)

c 🔊 5.1 Listen and check. Then listen again and repeat the words.

4 READING

a Read the story.

The fisherman and the banker

An American banker was on holiday abroad. He was walking on a beautiful beach near a small village. He saw a fisherman in his boat with a few fish in it.

'Great fish!' he said. 'How long did it take you to catch them?'

'Not very long,' answered the fisherman.

'Why didn't you stay at sea longer to catch some more?' asked the banker.

'There are just enough fish here to feed my family,' answered the fisherman.

Then the American asked, 'But what do you do the rest of the time?'

'I sleep late, I fish a little, I play with my kids, and I relax. In the evening, I go to see my friends in the village. We drink wine and play the guitar. I'm busier than you think. Life here isn't as…'

The American interrupted him. 'I have an MBA from Harvard University and I can help you. You're not fishing as much as you can. If you start fishing for longer periods of time, you'll get enough money from selling the fish to buy a bigger boat. Then with the money you'll get from catching and selling more fish, you could buy a second boat, and then a third one, and so on. Then instead of selling your fish to shops, you could sell them directly to a fish factory, or even open your own factory. Then you'll be able to leave your little village for the city, and finally move to New York, where you could direct the company.'

'How long will that take?' asked the fisherman.

'About 15 to 20 years,' answered the banker.

'And then?'

'Then it gets more interesting,' said the American, smiling and talking more quickly. 'When the moment comes, you can put your company on the stock market and you will make millions.'

'Millions? But then what?'

'Then you can retire, live in a small village by the sea, go to the beach, sleep late, play with your kids…'

b Mark the sentences T (true) or F (false).

1 The fisherman needed to catch more fish. _F_
2 The American thought he was very busy. _F_
3 The American wanted him to work harder. _T_
4 He told the fisherman to buy more boats. _T_
5 The American said that he couldn't live in New York. _F_
6 The American promised the fisherman a lot of money. _F_ _T_

5 LISTENING

a 🔊 5.2 Listen to five speakers talking about how their lives have changed. Who…?

1 has just started working from home ___
2 has had a baby ___
3 has lost his / her job ___
4 has moved to a different country _1_
5 has retired ___

b Listen again. Which two people are happiest about the changes?

_____

_____

Who is the least happy?

_____

USEFUL WORDS AND PHRASES

Learn these words and phrases.

abbreviations /əbriːviˈeɪʃnz/

characters /ˈkærəktəz/

nowadays /ˈnaʊədeɪz/

story /ˈstɔːri/

irritable /ˈɪrɪtəbl/

patient (opp *impatient*) /ˈpeɪʃnt/

queue /kjuː/

stressed /strest/

stressful /ˈstresfl/

tips /tɪps/

5B Superlative cities

1 GRAMMAR superlatives (+ *ever* + present perfect)

a Complete the sentences with the superlative of an adjective from the box.

~~bad~~	exciting	far	friendly	~~good~~
safe	ugly	wet		

1 The traffic is awful in the town centre. The ___*best*___ way to travel around is by underground.

2 It rains a lot here in the Spring. The ___*wettest*___ month is April.

3 The ___*farthest*___ I've ever driven is from London to Edinburgh. It took me eight hours.

4 It was the ___*worst*___ hotel I've ever stayed in. The service was awful, so we only spent one night there.

5 The ___*ugliest*___ buildings are in the new town. They really aren't nice to look at.

6 The streets are very dangerous at night. The ___*safest*___ place to be is in the hotel.

7 The ___*most exciting*___ part of our tour was in Rio de Janeiro. We saw the first day of the carnival.

8 The ___*friendliest*___ city I've ever visited is Vancouver. I found the people very helpful.

b Circle the correct word or phrase.

1 That hotel has the **dirtier** / **dirtiest** rooms I have ever seen.

2 It's the **most interesting** / **more interesting** museum in Edinburgh.

3 This is the **more expensive** / **most expensive** souvenir I've ever bought.

4 That restaurant serves the **better** / **best** pasta we've ever eaten.

5 The summer is the **busyest** / **busiest** time of year.

c Write sentences with *ever*.

1 He / rude waiter / I / meet
   He's the rudest waiter I've ever met.

2 That / fast car / I / drive
   That's the *fastest* car I ever *have* driven.

3 It / beautiful building / we / see
   It's the most beautiful building we ever *have* seen.

4 That / healthy meal / he / eat
   That's the healthiest meal he ever *has* eaten.

5 It / good photograph / you / take
   It's the best photograph you ever *have* taken.

6 This / exciting sport / I / do
   This is the most exciting sport I ever *have* done.

7 That / bad flight / we / have
   That's the worst flight we ever *have* had.

8 This / interesting city / I / visit
   This is the most interesting city, I ever *have* visited.

2 VOCABULARY describing a town or city

a Complete the description of Llandudno.

Llandudno is a town in the [1]n*orth* of Wales on the [2]c *ost* of the Irish Sea. It is about 35 miles [3]w *est* of Liverpool. It has a [4] *population* of about 21,000, and is [5]f *amous* as a seaside resort.

b Complete the sentences with the opposite of the adjectives in brackets.

1 Some of the buildings in the centre are quite m*odern*. (old)

2 Los Angeles is a very p*oluted* city – there are so many cars. (clean)

3 New York is a very s*afe* city these days. (dangerous)

4 Mumbai is an extremely n*oisy* city. (quiet)

5 Where's the most b_____ place you've ever been to? (interesting)

6 The subway in Tokyo is very c*rowded*. (empty)

c Circle the different word.

1	cathedral	church	shopping centre
2	mosque	temple	town hall
3	market	castle	department store
4	statue	palace	museum

3 PRONUNCIATION word stress

a 🔊5.3 Listen and underline the stressed syllable.

1 beau|ti|ful
2 crow|ded
3 dan|ge|rous
4 ex|ci|ting
5 fright|en|ing
6 ge|ne|rous
7 in|tere|sting
8 po|llu|ted
9 ro|man|tic

b Listen again and repeat the words.

swim – swum
understand – understood
speak – spoken
~~se~~ – seen
~~sit~~ – ~~sited~~ sat
~~take~~ – taken
~~show~~ – shown

4 LISTENING

a 🔊5.4 Listen to a radio travel programme about the Republic of Croatia. Tick (✓) the places that are mentioned in the programme.

1 Split ✓
2 Dubrovnik ☐
3 Rijeka ☐
4 Zagreb ☐
5 Trogir ☐
6 the islands ☐

b Listen again and mark the sentences T (true) or F (false).

1 Zagreb is an old city. *T*
2 50,000 people live in Dubrovnik. __
3 The palace is outside the city. __
4 You can get a ferry to visit the islands. __
5 The best time to visit is July and August. __

USEFUL WORDS AND PHRASES

Learn these words and phrases.

architecture /ˈɑːkɪtektʃə/
culture /ˈkʌltʃə/
inhabitants /ɪnˈhæbɪtənts/
without /wɪˈðaʊt/
nightlife /ˈnaɪtlaɪf/
several /ˈsevrəl/
foreign /ˈfɒrən/
romantic /rəʊˈmæntɪk/
rude /ruːd/
pretend (to do sth) /prɪˈtend/

I've been on a diet for two weeks
and all I've lost is fourteen days.

Totie Fields, American actress

5C How much is too much?

1 VOCABULARY health and the body

Complete the sentences with the words in the box.

~~anxious~~ bones brain faces illness prevent ~~skin~~

1 I'm ___anxious___ about my uncle's health because he's been ill for a long time.
2 People suffering from a serious __illness__ often stay in hospital for a long time.
3 You need to cover your __skin__ with sunscreen when you sunbathe.
4 You can tell they've been in the sun – their __faces__ are very red.
5 When you're old, your __bones__ can break more easily.
6 Coffee can sometimes __prevent__ you from sleeping.
7 My grandmother can't walk very well, but her __brain__ is still active.

2 GRAMMAR quantifiers, too, not enough

a Complete the sentences with *a few*, *a little*, *much*, *many* or *a lot of*.

1 She's quite overweight because she eats __a lot of__ sweets.
2 Can I ask you __a few__ questions about your diet? It won't take long.
3 Her children don't have a healthy diet – they don't eat __many__ vegetables.
4 How __much__ sugar do you have in your coffee?
5 Could I have __a little__ more tea, please?
6 I don't eat __much__ fruit – I need to eat more.
7 How __many__ hours do you spend in front of the TV every day?
8 __A little__ time in the sun is good for you, but no more than 15 minutes.
9 He's in his last year at school, so he gets __a lot of__ homework.
10 I only drink __a few__ cups of coffee a day – maybe two or three.

b Circle the correct phrase.

1 I can't go to the party. I'm **too** / **too much** ill.
2 I'm not very good at basketball. I'm not **enough tall** / **tall enough**.
3 I couldn't live in the UK. It rains **too many** / **too much**.
4 I'm not going to finish my homework. I don't have **enough time** / **time enough**.
5 I can't sleep. I've eaten **too much** / **too many** chocolate.
6 I can't carry my shopping home. I have **too much** / **too many** bags.
7 I'm really unfit. I don't do **enough exercise** / **exercise enough**.
8 I'm always tired. I don't **enough sleep** / **sleep enough**.

3 PRONUNCIATION /ʌ/, /uː/, /aɪ/, /e/

a ⏺ 5.5 Listen and write the words in the chart.

any diet ~~enough~~ few food healthy like many much none quite too

1 ʌ up	enough		
2 uː boot			
3 aɪ bike			
4 e egg			

b Listen again and repeat the words.

4 READING

a Read the newspaper article. Which one of these fruits and vegetables do not count towards your five a day?

beans ☑   potatoes ☒
peaches ☐   cucumber ☐
carrots ☑   peas ☐
plums ☐   pineapple ☑

b Read the article again and mark the sentences T (true) or F (false).

1 The campaign to eat more healthy food in the UK is called Six a Day. *F*

2 Fruit in a can isn't good for you. *F*

3 Frozen vegetables don't count towards your five a day. *f*

4 Only 100% pure fruit juice counts as a portion. *F*

5 One mandarin orange counts as one portion. *F* 2 piece

6 You have to eat many tomatoes to get one portion. *F*

7 A large spoonful of vegetables doesn't count as a portion. *T*

c Look at the highlighted words. What do you think they mean? Check with your dictionary.

5 LISTENING

a 🔊 5.6 Listen to two people doing a quiz about body age. How old is Alice? What is her body age?

b Listen again and complete the sentences.

1 Alice walks __*quite a lot*__ every day.

2 She does _____ sport or exercise.

3 She doesn't eat _____ fast food.

4 She eats _____ fruit and vegetables.

5 She's a very _____ person.

6 She's _____ stressed.

7 She sees _____ close friends regularly.

8 She doesn't have _____ time for herself.

USEFUL WORDS AND PHRASES

Learn these words and phrases.

bones /bəʊnz/   skills /skɪlz/
brain /breɪn/   skin /skɪn/
face /feɪs/   sunlight /'sʌnlaɪt/
illness /'ɪlnəs/   sunscreen /'sʌnskriːn/
prevent /prɪ'vent/   anxious /'æŋkʃəs/

Five a Day

How much fruit do you eat every day? And how many vegetables? Food experts today think that we don't have enough of these foods in our diet and they say that we eat too much fat and sugar. This is why the World Health Organization has started a campaign to encourage us to eat more fruit and vegetables. The campaign in the UK is called Five a Day.

Why eat fruit and vegetables?

Fruit and vegetables are full of important vitamins and minerals which our bodies need to be healthy. Scientific studies have shown that eating a lot of them can prevent some illnesses like diabetes and obesity. Also, fruit and vegetables don't contain much fat and they don't have many calories, so they help to keep us slim.

What counts?

Nearly all fruit and vegetables count towards your five a day, except potatoes. The food can be fresh, frozen, or in a can, like peaches or peas. It can be raw, cooked, or even dried, like raisins or banana chips. A glass of 100% fruit juice with no added sugar also counts as one portion.

How much is a portion?

A portion of fresh fruit or vegetables depends on the size of the food. In the case of small-sized fruit like plums or mandarin oranges, one portion is two pieces of fruit. A piece of medium-sized fruit like an apple, an orange, or a pear also counts as one portion. With larger fruit like melon and pineapple, one portion is a 5 cm slice. We use the same method for calculating portions with vegetables. In the case of salad vegetables, a medium-sized tomato or a 5cm piece of cucumber count as one portion each. For smaller, cooked vegetables like beans and carrots, one portion is three large spoonfuls of vegetables.

1 VOCABULARY shopping

Match the prices.

1 79c   [c]   a fifty-nine pence
2 €30.49   [   ]   b thirteen pounds ninety-nine
3 $3.89   [   ]   c seventy-nine cents
4 59p   [   ]   d thirty euros forty-nine
5 £13.99   [   ]   e three dollars eighty-nine

2 TAKING SOMETHING BACK TO A SHOP

Complete the dialogue.

A Can I help you, [1]m*adam* ?
B Yes, I [2]b*ought* this sweater yesterday.
A Yes, I remember. Is there a [3]pr*oblem* ?
B Yes, I'm [4]af*raid* it's too small.
A What [5]s*ize* is it?
B It's a [6]s*mall* . Do you have a [7]m*edium* ?
A I'll go and [8]s_____ . Just a minute. I'm [9]s*orry* but we don't have this sweater in your size. But we do have this one and it's the same price. Or you can have a [10]r_____ .
B Erm…I'll take this one then, please. Can I try it on?
A Yes, of course. The [11]ch_____ r_____ are over there. Is everything OK?
B Yes, this one fits perfectly.
A Good. Do you have the [12]r_____ for the other sweater?
B Yes, here you are.
A Brilliant.

3 SOCIAL ENGLISH

Order the dialogue.

A Have you had a good day?   1
B OK. For what time?   4
A Sure.   7
B Can we make it a bit earlier? Say, seven thirty? 6
A Why don't we go out for dinner? I could book a restaurant.   3
B OK. I'll go and have a shower then. 8
A Eight o'clock?   5
B Oh, you know. Working! But it was OK.   2

4 READING

a Read the text. Where could you…?

1 make a toy   _FAO Schwarz_
2 try on a designer bracelet   _____
3 buy something for when you have a shower   _____
4 get a tattoo   _____

Fifth Avenue Shopping:

Fifth Avenue is one of the most expensive shopping streets in the world. Most of the world's luxury boutiques are located here, including Gucci, Prada, Armani, and Cartier. It is also home to huge department stores like Lord & Taylor, Barneys, and Bergdorf Goodman. Most shops open daily from 10 a.m. to 7 p.m., starting later on Sundays. Here are some of the most well known:

FAO SCHWARZ

This world-famous toy store is popular with tourists and New Yorkers. The amazing Grand Hall has more than 20,000 coloured lights and there's also a giant dance-on piano keyboard and an enormous candy store. Big kids can have lots of fun in the do-it-yourself department, where they can even design their own doll.

RICKY'S

This ultra-fashionable beauty shop has been selling the latest cosmetics, hair and bath products for nearly two decades. Products range from the most expensive to the most ecological, so there's something for everybody. Upstairs, check out the fun clothing and accessories. You can also get temporary henna tattoos.

TIFFANY & CO

This exclusive jeweller's has occupied its current location since 1940. Customers can admire the designer jewellery on the first floor before taking the elevator upstairs to choose an engagement ring. You can buy elegant table, glass, and silverware on the fourth floor, and there are less pricey items on the third floor.

b Read the text again. Match the highlighted words to their meanings.

1 the set of keys on a piano   _keyboard_
2 very expensive   _____
3 scarves, belts, gloves, etc.   _____
4 an agreement to get married   _____
5 very big   _____
6 the activity of making things on your own   _do it yourself_

A pessimist is someone who is pleased with bad experiences because they show he was right.

Heinz Ruhmann, German actor and film director

1 GRAMMAR *will / won't* (predictions)

Complete the dialogues with *will / won't* and a verb from the box. Use contractions.

not remember   ~~fall~~   not sell   forget   not win   miss

A I'm going climbing next weekend.
B It's very dangerous. You *'ll fall* _____ .

A I'm playing in the tennis final tomorrow.
B The other player is very good. You _____ .

A I'm going to study all evening.
B It's a waste of time. You _____ anything in the morning.

A I told Nick that it's Jane's birthday on Friday.
B You know Nick! He _____ .

A I'm going to put my MP3 player on eBay.
B It's too old. You _____ it.

A I'm getting the 8.50 train.
B It's leaving in five minutes. You _____ it.

2 VOCABULARY opposite verbs

Write the opposite verb in each space. Be careful – use the correct verb form.

1 **arrive**
   You won't ___*leave*___ on time.

2 **teach**
   We're going to _____ English in Canada.

3 **fail**
   I don't think he _____ all of his exams.

4 **Push**
   _____ the door to open it.

5 **mend**
   I've _____ my glasses.

6 **lend**
   Can I _____ a pen, please?

7 **win**
   I think he's going to _____ the race.

8 **turn off**
   Can you _____ the light, please?

9 **get**
   I _____ more than 50 emails yesterday.

10 **lose**
   I've _____ some money!

3 PRONUNCIATION *'ll, won't*

🔊 **6.1** Listen and repeat. <u>C</u>opy the <u>rhy</u>thm.

1 I'll **learn a lot**.
2 He'll **meet** somebody **new**.
3 **You'll** have a **good time**.
4 She **won't** get the **job**.
5 They **won't lend** you the <u>**money**</u>.
6 We **won't a<u>rrive</u>** on **time**.

4 READING

a Read the horoscopes for this month. Answer the questions.

Horoscopes

 AQUARIUS Jan 21–Feb 19

You'll be lucky in love this month! You'll meet someone new at work, which will be the start of something special. The colour red will bring you good fortune.

 PISCES Feb 20–Mar 20

Close family will be important this month. Try to spend more time with them and they'll be very glad to see you. The colour green will bring you luck with money.

 ARIES Mar 21–Apr 20

You'll have to be very careful with money this month, and avoid buying any clothes. However, you'll get a nice surprise at the end of the month. The colour blue will bring you luck.

 TAURUS Apr 21–May 21

You'll have a very busy social life this month! Your friends will be taking you out all the time, and you'll make many new ones too. Orange will be your lucky colour.

 GEMINI May 22–June 21

You won't have a very good month at work. Your boss will give you some bad news, but don't worry: you won't be unemployed. Work hard and next month will be better. Purple will be your lucky colour.

 CANCER June 22–July 23

This will be a great month for going away! You'll win a holiday, so have your passport ready. You'll also travel a lot in your own country and you'll visit some old friends. Yellow will be your lucky colour.

1 Who will do a lot of travelling this month?   *Cancer*
2 Who will have problems with their job?   _____
3 Who won't go shopping?   _____
4 Whose lucky colour will be red?   _____
5 Who will go out a lot this month?   _____

b <u>Underline</u> five words you don't know. Use your dictionary to look up their meaning and pronunciation.

5 LISTENING

a ◗ 6.2 Listen to a conversation about horoscopes. What are Matt and Amy's star signs?

b Listen again and complete the sentences with A (Amy) or M (Matt).

1 ___A___ believes in horoscopes.
2 _____ doesn't believe in horoscopes.
3 _____ has a problem with someone.
4 _____ is worried about the horoscope.
5 _____ was born in January.
6 _____'s horoscope is good.
7 _____ has a meeting the next day.

Vote for the man who promises least –
he'll be the least disappointing.

Bernard Baruch, American political adviser

6B I'll never forget you

1 GRAMMAR will / won't (promises, offers, decisions)

a Write sentences using the pictures and prompts. Use *Shall I | I'll | I won't*.

1 call / you tomorrow
_   I'll call you tomorrow_ .
2 lend / you some money?
_____ ?
3 have / the chicken
_____ .
4 take / your coat?
_____ ?
5 turn off / air conditioning?
_____ ?
6 not / be late
_____ .

b Are these sentences promises (P), decisions (D), or offers (O)?

1 I'll drive you home.   _O_
2 I'll remember to tell her.   __
3 Shall I get you some water?   __
4 I'll help you clean your room, if you like.   __
5 I'll have the chocolate cake, please.   __
6 I won't tell your girlfriend.   __

2 VOCABULARY verb + *back*

Complete the sentences with the verbs in the box.

~~call~~   come   give   pay   send   take

1 **A** Jack phoned while you were out.
  B Thanks. I'll ___*call*___ him back in a minute.
2 **A** Do you want to borrow some money?
  B Yes, please. I'll _____ you back next week.
3 **A** The person you want to see isn't here. She's at lunch.
  B That's OK. I'll _____ back later.
4 **A** It's a really nice top, but it doesn't fit me.
  B Don't worry. I'll _____ it back to the shop and change it.
5 **A** Have you finished that book I lent you?
  B Yes. I'll _____ it back to you tomorrow.
6 **A** That toy car you bought on the internet doesn't work.
  B Doesn't it? I'll _____ it back, then.

3 PRONUNCIATION word stress: two-syllable verbs

a ◑6.3 Listen and under<u>line</u> the stressed syllables. ⃝Circle⃝ the words which are stressed on the second syllable.

1 <u>wo</u>|rry   ⃝re|<u>lax</u>⃝   ⃝be|<u>come</u>⃝
2 de|cide   e|mail   pro|mise
3 prac|tise   li|sten   re|pair
4 bo|rrow   for|get   a|gree
5 sun|bathe   in|vite   com|plain

b Listen and check. Then listen again and repeat the words.

4 READING

a Read the text. What did Paul learn from his experience?

An expensive lesson

My name's Paul, and this happened to me when I was visiting a friend in Paris.

I was getting off the Eurostar train at the Gare du Nord station when a man came up to me. He was wearing a suit and he looked quite respectable. 'Do you speak English?' he asked. He had a French accent, but he said he was a banker from Montreal in the French-speaking part of Canada. Then he told me he had a problem. 'I'm here in Paris with my wife and our three children, and we don't have enough money for a hotel. You see, my wife tried to get money from a cash machine, but she couldn't remember our PIN number. She used the wrong number three times, so the machine kept her card. Could you help me?' I wasn't sure, so I asked to see his passport. 'My passport is with my wife. She's waiting in a café with the children. We only need €65 for the night and I promise I'll pay you back.' By this time the man was actually crying, so I thought he was telling the truth. I agreed to lend him the money and I wrote down his name, email address, and phone number in Montreal. Then we went to a cash machine and I gave him the money. He said thank you, gave me a big hug, and left. I never saw him or heard from him ever again.

I knew his story wasn't completely true. Why did a banker have only one bank card? Why didn't he tell me how he would pay me back? Were his wife and children really in the café, and did they even exist? But I was tired and in a foreign country, and I felt like I had to help him. I now know to be very careful who I talk to when I arrive somewhere new!

b Read the text. Number the sentences in the right order.

a Paul wrote down the man's contact details. ___

b The man explained his problem. ___

c The man's wife had his passport. ___

d Paul arrived in Paris. _1_

e Paul asked for the man's passport. ___

f A man started talking to him. ___

g Paul didn't hear from the man. ___

h Paul gave the man some money. ___

c Underline five words you don't know. Use your dictionary to look up their meaning and pronunciation.

5 LISTENING

a ◖)6.4 Listen to five speakers describing problems they have had abroad. What do the speakers have in common?

b Listen again and match the speakers with the sentences.

Speaker 1   _D_

Speaker 2   ___

Speaker 3   ___

Speaker 4   ___

Speaker 5   ___

A Next time, I'll check before I go.

B I'll buy my own in future.

C I won't let anyone in another time.

D I won't do anyone any favours in the future.

E I won't go out with anyone I don't know again.

USEFUL WORDS AND PHRASES

Learn these words and phrases.

hurt /hɜːt/

previous /ˈpriːviəs/

double portion /ˈdʌbl pɔːʃn/

ice cream sundae /aɪs kriːm ˈsʌndeɪ/

get engaged /get ɪnˈgeɪdʒd/

get in touch /get ɪn ˈtʌtʃ/

in their twenties /ɪn ðeə ˈtwentiz/

Only in our dreams are we free.
The rest of the time we need wages.

Terry Pratchett, British writer

6C The meaning of dreaming

1 GRAMMAR review of verb forms: present, past, and future

a Complete the dialogues with the correct form of the verbs in brackets. Use contractions where possible.

1 **A** *Are* you *going to go out* tonight? (go out)

   B No, I'm really tired. I'm __*going to go*__ to bed early. (go)

2 **A** What time _____ you usually _____ to bed? (go)

   B At 10.30. Then I _____ for an hour before I go to sleep. (read)

3 **A** Do you think England _____ tonight? (win)

   B No, I think they _____. (lose)

4 **A** What _____ you _____ at midnight last night? (do)

   B I _____ TV. (watch)

5 **A** _____ you ever _____ that you were flying? (dream)

   B No, I _____ never _____ that dream. (have)

6 **A** What _____ you _____? It's 5 o'clock in the morning! (do)

   B I can't sleep so I _____. (read)

7 **A** _____ you _____ well last night? (sleep)

   B No, I _____ in the middle of the night, and I couldn't go back to sleep. (wake up)

8 **A** What time _____ you _____ tomorrow? (leave)

   B I'm _____ at 8 o'clock. (go)

b Complete the text with the correct form of the verbs in brackets. Use contractions where necessary.

What colour are our dreams?

[1] __*Do*__ we __*dream*__ (dream) in colour or in black and white? People argued for many years about this question and scientists [2] _____ (do) a lot of research into this question. One of these scientists is a psychologist who [3] _____ (work) at Dundee University. Her name is Eva Murzyn, and right now she [4] _____ (study) the effect of television on our dreams. Eva [5] _____ just _____ (publish) the results of her latest study.

Sixty people [6] _____ (help) Eva with her research. They completed a questionnaire and kept a diary of their dreams. She [7] _____ (choose) people who were either under 25 or over 55. When Eva analyzed their diaries, she [8] _____ (discover) that the younger people usually dreamt in colour, whereas the older group often [9] _____ (have) black and white dreams. Eva thinks that this is because the older group [10] _____ (see) programmes in black and white when they were young. She believes that something happened to their brains while they [11] _____ (watch) TV at that time.

2 VOCABULARY adjectives + prepositions

Circle the correct preposition.

1 Sleeping eight hours a night is good **for** / **to** you.
2 She's angry **with** / **at** him because he forgot her birthday.
3 The village of Cheddar is famous **to** / **for** its cheese.
4 I'm very bad **in** / **at** drawing.
5 Be nice **to** / **at** me today because I'm in a bad mood.
6 We aren't interested **about** / **in** motor racing.
7 My little sister is afraid **of** / **to** big dogs.
8 The new boss is very different **of** / **from** our old one.

3 PRONUNCIATION the letters *ow*

a 6.5 Listen and circle the word with a different sound.

aʊ  owl				
1	brown	know	how	town
2	blow	snow	now	show
3	borrow	crowded	shower	towel
4	low	throw	window	down

b Listen and check. Then listen again and repeat the words.

4 LISTENING

a 6.6 Listen to a radio programme about recurring dreams. Number the dreams in the order you hear them.

__ You are flying.
1 You are running.
__ You can't escape.
__ You are lost.
__ You are falling.

b Listen again and match the interpretations with the dreams.

Dream 1	*e*	a You don't know what to do in your life.
Dream 2		b You can't change a difficult situation.
Dream 3		c Your life has improved in some way.
Dream 4		d You don't want your life to change.
Dream 5		~~e You don't want to face a problem.~~

USEFUL WORDS AND PHRASES

Learn these words and phrases.

champagne /ʃæm'peɪn/
flowers /'flaʊəz/
owl /aʊl/
psychoanalyst /saɪkəʊ'ænəlɪst/
violin /vaɪə'lɪn/
freezing /'friːzɪŋ/
be frightened of /bi 'fraɪtnd ɒv/
dream about /'driːm əbaʊt/
be successful /bi sək'sesfl/

I love your daughter, Jack. I love her more than anything. But frankly sir, I'm a little terrified of being your son-in-law.

Greg in the film Meet the Parents, *2000*

7A How to...

1 GRAMMAR uses of the infinitive with *to*

a Complete the sentences with the infinitive (with *to*) of a verb from the box.

---
not do   find   not finish   rent   see   not tell   ~~wash up~~
---

1 John's very polite. He offered ___*to wash up*___ after the meal.
2 Thanks for coming. We hope _____ you again soon.
3 She wasn't enjoying the lasagne, so she decided _____ it.
4 My boyfriend is unemployed. He needs _____ a job.
5 I'll tell you what she said, but please promise _____ anybody.
6 I'm sorry I shouted at you. I'll try _____ it again.
7 They want to live together. They're planning _____ a flat.

b Write sentences using the adjective and the correct form of the verb.

1 **nice / meet**
   Hello! How ___*nice to meet*___ you.
2 **difficult / talk**
   Do you find it _____ to my mum?
3 **easy / buy**
   It's _____ presents for my girlfriend.
4 **important / not say**
   It's _____ the wrong thing.
5 **great / hear**
   Thanks for calling. It was _____ from you.
6 **fun / be**
   It's _____ with your family.
7 **kind / invite**
   Her parents were very _____ him.

c Complete the sentences with *to* and a verb.

1 He gave them some chocolates ___*to say*___ thank you.
2 They're going to evening classes _____ Chinese.
3 We called the restaurant _____ a table.
4 He told us a joke _____ us laugh.
5 I went to a cash machine _____ some money.
6 Do you use your phone _____ photos?

d Complete the sentences with a question word from the box, and *to* + the verb in brackets.

~~how~~   how many   how much   what   when   where
---

1 She gave me her address, but I don't know ___*how to get*___ there. (get)
2 My brother is always busy so I don't know _____ him. (call)
3 My mum asked me to get some eggs, but she didn't say _____. (buy)
4 We'd like to travel around the world, but we don't know _____ first. (go)
5 She wants to go to university, but she doesn't know _____. (study)
6 Who's going to be here for lunch? I have pasta, but I need to know _____. (make)

2 VOCABULARY verbs + infinitive

Complete the text with a verb from the box in the past tense.

---
forget   try   not want   promise   pretend   learn   offer   plan   ~~start~~   need   not remember
---

Charlie wasn't happy at his work so he [1] ___*started*___ to apply for a new job. Soon, one company called him and [2] _____ to give him an interview. Charlie [3] _____ to tell his boss, so he [4] _____ to be ill. He told his boss that he had a stomach ache, and he [5] _____ to go to the doctor's. His boss [6] _____ to call him later to ask him how he was. Charlie was really hoping to get the job, so he was a bit nervous. He [7] _____ to drive to the interview, but there was a lot of traffic. In the end, he took the underground and was very late, and he [8] _____ to turn his mobile phone off. Unfortunately, it rang while he was in the interview, but Charlie didn't answer it. However when his boss called later he [9] _____ to act ill. The next morning, his boss said, 'I'd like to see you in my office.' Charlie [10] _____ to apologize, but his boss was very angry and Charlie nearly lost his job. But he [11] _____ an important lesson: not to lie to his boss again.

3 PRONUNCIATION linking, weak form of *to*

a Practise saying the sentences.

1 We want to know.

2 They hoped to win.

3 He promised to call.

4 I don't know what to do.

5 She forgot to go.

6 It's important to remember.

7 I learned to swim.

8 He started to cry.

b 🔊 7.1 Listen and check. Then listen again and repeat the sentences.

4 READING

a Read the article. Is the writer generally positive or negative about mothers-in-law?

The truth about mothers-in-law

Although it's men who tell jokes about them, mothers-in-law are usually less popular with their daughters-in-law than with their sons-in-law. A recent study of 49 married couples found that two thirds of wives interviewed said that their mothers-in-law caused them 'unhappiness and stress', compared with 15% of the husbands.

There are a number of reasons for this. First of all, there is the question of experience. A mother-in-law has already brought up a family of her own, so she feels that she has a lot of knowledge to pass on. In this situation, it is very difficult for her to keep quiet. However, when a daughter-in-law is a new mother, she usually wants to find her own way of doing things. She often interprets her mother-in-law's advice as criticism, which can cause a conflict.

Secondly, there is the case of the husband. Both women care for him, although each of them loves him in a different way. On the one hand, he is the mother-in-law's son and she obviously wants the best for him. On the other hand, he is the wife's partner, and she wants him to support her. Both women can get very upset if they see the man taking sides, and this can cause an argument.

However, mothers-in-law actually have a lot to offer, despite their reputation for causing trouble. They are generally excellent babysitters, and they don't mind helping with the housework. As long as they have their own independent lives and help out only when needed, mothers-in-law can play a very useful role in any family. The important thing is that they should not get too involved in their sons' and daughters' relationship so that nobody feels bad.

b Read the article again and choose the best answer.

1 What did the study find out about mothers-in-law?
   a More men than women have problems with them.
   b More men than women tell jokes about them.
   ⓒ More women than men have problems with them.

2 What advice do mothers-in-law try to give their daughters-in-law?
   a How to look after their husband.
   b How to bring up children.
   c How to do housework.

3 According to the article, which situation makes daughters-in-law angry?
   a When their husband agrees with his mother.
   b When their husband talks to his mother.
   c When their husband argues with his mother.

4 Which women make the best mothers-in-law?
   a Those who are really close to their son.
   b Those who don't have a life of their own.
   c Those who know when to offer help.

c Underline five words you don't know. Use your dictionary to look up their meaning and pronunciation.

5 LISTENING

a 🔊 7.2 Listen to a conversation between two people about a ban on mother-in-law jokes. Do they agree in the end? _____

b Listen again and complete the sentences with D (Dave) or J (Jane).

1 *D* thinks the ban is ridiculous.

2 ___ thinks that the jokes are offensive.

3 ___ thinks that it's important to have a sense of humour.

4 ___ makes a joke.

5 ___ thinks that the jokes don't show respect for parents.

6 ___ mentions a historical fact about mothers-in-law.

7 ___ quotes a historical joke.

8 ___ says that the jokes are sexist.

USEFUL WORDS AND PHRASES

Learn these words and phrases.

advice /əd'vaɪs/

tactic /'tæktɪk/

greet /griːt/

survive /sə'vaɪv/

honest /'ɒnɪst/

absolutely delicious /æbsəluːtli dɪ'lɪʃəs/

be punctual /bi 'pʌŋktʃuəl/

make conversation /meɪk kɒnvə'seɪʃn/

shake (sbd's) hand /ʃeɪk 'hænd/

(make) the right impression /ðə 'raɪt ɪmpreʃn/

Happiness is when what you think, what you say,
and what you do are all in harmony.

Mahatma Gandhi, Indian political leader

7B Being happy

1 GRAMMAR uses of the gerund (verb + -ing)

a Complete the sentences with the -ing form of the verbs in brackets.

1 I hate ___being___ (be) cold. I find it really depressing.
2 You spend too long _____ (play) video games.
3 We stopped _____ (study) French because we didn't like the classes.
4 He's celebrating because he's finished _____ (write) his book.
5 It started _____ (snow) during the night while we were asleep.
6 I'm bored. I feel like _____ (go) for a walk.
7 My parents have bought a house by a beach, because they love _____ (swim).
8 I don't mind _____ (get) up early in the morning.
9 Kathy really enjoys _____ (listen) to her iPod.
10 The best thing about _____ (use) the bus is _____ (not drive) in busy traffic.

b Match the sentence beginnings and endings.

1 Do you ever dream of [c]
2 Are you interested in [ ]
3 Please don't leave without [ ]
4 She isn't very good at [ ]
5 We ended the evening by [ ]
6 I'm really looking forward to [ ]

a doing some part-time work?
b seeing you tonight.
c ~~stopping work and retiring?~~
d thanking everybody for coming.
e saying goodbye to me.
f parking her boyfriend's car.

c Complete the text with the -ing form of the verbs in the box.

drive   exercise   get up   go   have   imagine   leave   listen   read   ~~send~~   stay   take   turn   ~~write~~

What makes you feel good?

Here are some more texts from our readers.

1 [1] ___Writing___ and then [2] ___sending___ a funny email or text message to my friends. And of course, [3] _____ their faces when they read it.

2 I really like [4] _____ at night when there's no traffic, [5] _____ to my favourite music. I feel completely free.

3 [6] _____ in bed on Sunday morning and [7] _____ the newspaper. Then [8] _____ very late and [9] _____ my dog for a long walk.

4 I enjoy [10] _____ to the gym and really [11] _____ hard, then [12] _____ a long hot shower followed by a nice cold drink. There's nothing better.

5 [13] _____ off my computer at the end of the day and [14] _____ work! It's the best moment of the day. I love it!

d Complete the text with the correct form of the verbs in brackets (-*ing* form or infinitive).

Reading the digital way

Many of us who love ¹ _reading_ (read) are changing our habits. Today, a lot of us have decided
² _____ (use) e-readers, and so we've stopped
³ _____ (buy) traditional books.

E-readers have a number of advantages. They are very easy ⁴ _____ (carry), so they are ideal for people who like ⁵ _____ (travel). If you're abroad, and you don't have anything ⁶ _____ (read), you don't need
⁷ _____ (look for) a bookshop that has books in your language – you can download it as a digital book. In addition to this, e-readers are very private, so you don't need ⁸ _____ (show) people what you are reading. Finally, when you finish ⁹ _____ (read) a book, you no longer have to find room for it on a bookshelf.

However, there are some disadvantages. Some people say their eyes hurt if they spend a long time ¹⁰ _____ (look) at the screen. Also, you have to be careful
¹¹ _____ (not lose) your e-reader or you'll lose all your books. As well as this, if a friend would like
¹² _____ (borrow) a book you've read, you can't offer ¹³ _____ (lend) it to them. With an e-reader, you can only go on ¹⁴ _____ (read) as long as the battery lasts, so you have to remember ¹⁵ _____ (take) your charger with you and you mustn't forget
¹⁶ _____ (charge) the battery.

2 VOCABULARY verbs + gerund

Match the sentences 1–6 with definitions a–f.

1 He hates doing the housework. [c]
2 He feels like going for a run. [ ]
3 He doesn't mind cooking all the meals. [ ]
4 He's stopped playing football. [ ]
5 He spends hours chatting online. [ ]
6 He loves being with his friends. [ ]

a He doesn't do it any more.
b It's OK for him to do it.
c He really doesn't like it.
d He does it a lot.
e He wants to do it now.
f He really likes it.

3 PRONUNCIATION the letter *i*

a Circle the word with a different sound.

fish	1	miss (mind) skin with
bike	2	promise hire kind size
fish	3	practise finish service surprise
bike	4	arrive engine invite online

b 7.3 Listen and check. Then listen again nd repeat the words.

4 LISTENING

a 7.4 Listen to five speakers talking about when and where they sing. How many of the speakers don't enjoy singing?

b Listen again and match the speakers with sentences A–E.

Speaker 1 _C_
Speaker 2 ___
Speaker 3 ___
Speaker 4 ___
Speaker 5 ___

A He / She does a lot of singing at work.
B He / She doesn't mind singing badly in front of other people.
C He / She enjoys singing at home.
D He / She likes singing when he/she is travelling.
E He / She was in a choir at school.

7C Learn a language in a month!

1 GRAMMAR *have to, don't have to, must, mustn't*

a Look at the pictures. Complete the sentences with the correct form of *have to*.

1 **A** __Do__ teachers in your country __have to__ look smart?
B Not very smart. They _____ wear formal clothes, but they _____ look tidy.

2 **A** _____ British taxi drivers _____ go to university? Someone told me that.
B No. We _____ pass a special test, but we _____ go to university.

3 **A** _____ I _____ cook meals?
B No. You _____ do the cooking, but you _____ help the children to eat.

4 **A** _____ your husband _____ travel abroad in his job?
B No, he _____ travel abroad, but he _____ speak foreign languages.

b What do these signs mean? Write sentences with *must* or *mustn't*.

1 __You must__ pay in cash.
2 _____ turn left here.
3 _____ make a noise.
4 _____ use your mobile phone.
5 _____ stop here.
6 _____ play football here.

c Complete the sentences with *mustn't* or *don't have to*.

1 The museum is free. You __don't have to__ pay.
2 You have to wear smart clothes. You _____ wear jeans.
3 The speed limit is 120 km/h. You _____ drive faster.
4 Your hours will be 9–5 Monday to Friday. You _____ work at weekends.
5 That river is dangerous. You _____ swim in it.
6 It's a very small flat. You _____ clean it every day.

2 VOCABULARY modifiers: *a bit, really,* etc.

Order the words to make sentences.

1 translation / useful / Online / aren't / sites / very
__Online translation sites aren't very useful.__

2 to / quite / films / understand / It's / American / difficult
It's _____.

3 new / fast / speaks / Our / very / teacher
Our _____.

4 of / bit / those / unfriendly / a / students / Some / are
Some _____.

5 is / English / idea / books / a / really / Reading / good
Reading _____.

6 hard / incredibly / Chinese / to / It's / learn
It's _____.

3 PRONUNCIATION *must, mustn't*

🔊 7.5 Listen and repeat. <u>Copy</u> the <u>rhy</u>thm.

1 You **mustn't** take **photos**.
2 They **must make** the **exam easier**.
3 She **mustn't drive** a **car**.
4 He **must** be **early**.
5 We **mustn't talk** in the **library**.
6 You **must** take **one** pill **every day**.

4 READING

a Read the opinions about learning languages. Which do you think are the three best ideas?

What's the best way to…? Learn a language

This week we ask students from all over the world for their ideas.

Josef, Czech Republic

I think it's really hard to learn a language if you don't have anyone to talk to. I've joined a social networking site where I can chat in English to lots of other people like me. I'm more interested in using English to communicate than anything else, so I don't mind if my grammar isn't perfect.

Paolo, Portugal

I don't have time to go to an English class, but there's a great site on the internet which has classes in the form of podcasts. Every week, I download a few of these onto my phone, so that I can listen to the class when I'm going to and from work. I find the words and phrases that I have to listen to and repeat incredibly useful.

Marit, Norway

I'm a big fan of English pop music, so I spend a lot of time listening to different songs at home on my iPad. I've downloaded a new app that puts the lyrics on the screen and translates the song for you at the same time. I really enjoy learning English like this, and it's very good for my pronunciation, too.

Kiko, Japan

I can't afford to pay for one-to-one English classes, but I've found a great course online. I have to watch a short video, and then learn the grammar and vocabulary in it. If I have any questions, I can contact my online tutor who's very friendly. I'm really enjoying the course, and I've learned a lot from it.

Luis, Spain

I love books, and in my opinion, you can learn a lot of new words by reading in English. My journey to university is quite long, so I usually read books on my e-reader. You can click on difficult words and get a translation, which is very helpful.

Gloria, Brazil

My favourite way to learn a language is to go to a language school and join a class. There are classes for many levels of English, whether you're a beginner or you've been learning for a long time. It's great when you have other students in the class and you can learn and practise together, and of course having a teacher to help you is really important. It's good to do your homework too!

b Complete the sentences with the people's names.

1 _Marit_ thinks that listening to songs helps her pronunciation.
2 _____ says that reading can improve your vocabulary.
3 _____ has contact with an online teacher.
4 _____ thinks that speaking is more important than grammar.
5 _____ likes meeting and practising with other students.
6 _____ practises English mostly by listening.

5 LISTENING

a 🔊 7.6 Listen to a radio programme about the Cherokee language. On what gadgets can the Cherokee people use their language today?

_____

b Listen again and answer the questions.

1 How many languages exist in the world today?
   Nearly 6,000
2 By 2100, how many will disappear?
3 How many members of the Cherokee tribe could speak Cherokee when the plan started?
4 How many Cherokees were there?
5 When did Apple release iOS 4.1 with Cherokee as an official language?

USEFUL WORDS AND PHRASES

Learn these words and phrases.

experiment /ɪkˈsperɪmənt/
fees /fiːz/
voicemail /ˈvɔɪsmeɪl/
permitted /pəˈmɪtɪd/
obligatory /əˈblɪgətri/
complete beginner /kəmˈpliːt bɪˈgɪnə/
entrance fee /ˈentrəns ˈfiː/
intensive course /ɪnˈtensɪv kɔːs/
against the rules /ˈəgeɪnst ðə ruːlz/

Practical English At the pharmacy

1 VOCABULARY feeling ill

Complete the sentences.

1 Dan feels terrible. He thinks he has __*flu*__ (ULF).
2 I need to buy some tissues. I have a _____ (LCDO).
3 That fish wasn't very nice. Now I have a _____ _____ (DBA OCHMSTA).
4 You feel very hot. I think you have a _____ (EMRETUPETRA).
5 Please turn that music down. I have a _____ (CHAEHEDA).
6 Kate smokes too much. She has a _____ (OGUHC).

2 GOING TO A PHARMACY

Complete the dialogue with the words in the box.

allergic better every have ~~help~~ much often
symptoms take well

A Good afternoon. How can I [1] __*help*__?
B I'm not feeling very [2] _____.
A What are your [3] _____?
B I have a bad cough.
A Do you [4] _____ a temperature?
B No, I don't.
A Are you [5] _____ to any drugs?
B No, I don't think so.
A Take this cough medicine. It'll make you feel [6] _____.
B How much do I have to [7] _____?
A Ten ml [8] _____ six hours.
B Sorry? How [9] _____?
A Every six hours.
B OK, thanks. How [10] _____ is that?
A That's $4.50, please.

3 SOCIAL ENGLISH

Complete the sentences.

1 **A** That was a l_____ meal.
  B I'm gl_____ you enjoyed it.
2 **A** C_____ I have some more coffee, please?
  B There isn't any more. Anyway, drinking too much coffee isn't good f_____ you.
3 **A** I think I sh_____ go now.
  B Shall I take you home?
  A No, I'll walk. I'm s_____ I'll be fine.

4 READING

Match the signs 1–9 with their meaning A–I.

[1] E

Do not exceed the stated dose

[2]

[3]
Keep out of reach of children

[4]

[5]

Mind the step

[6]

[7]
May cause side effects

[8]
Not to be taken by infants

[9]
Take twice a day with a meal

A You must keep this medicine where children can't find it.
B You must not give this medicine to small children.
C You mustn't drink this water.
D You must take this medicine at breakfast and dinner.
E ~~You should be careful not to take too much of this medicine.~~
F You should be careful if you feel ill after taking this medicine.
G You mustn't smoke here.
H You should be careful or you might fall over.
I You have to turn your mobile off.

Advice is what you ask for when you already know the answer but wish you didn't.

Erica Jong, American writer

8A I don't know what to do!

1 GRAMMAR *should*

a Match the sentences with the pictures. Complete them with *should* or *shouldn't*.

1 She ___should___ eat her vegetables. [B]
2 She _____ wear a coat. ☐
3 'You _____ eat so much salt.' ☐
4 He _____ drive to work. ☐
5 'You _____ get some glasses.' ☐
6 She _____ carry heavy bags. ☐

b Complete the advice with *should* / *shouldn't* and a verb from the box.

~~buy~~ call drink give go see tell

1 You _shouldn't buy_ it because it won't fit you.
2 You _____ coffee all day.
3 You _____ to bed earlier.
4 You _____ a doctor immediately.
5 You _____ her how you feel.
6 You _____ them any sweets.
7 You _____ her and invite her to dinner.

c Read the problems A–G. Match them with the advice in **b**.

A I find it really difficult to get up in the morning, and I'm often late for work. My boss has noticed and she's quite angry with me. What should I do? [3]

B Yesterday, I hurt my foot while I was playing football. It didn't seem very serious at the time, but now my foot has gone black. What is your advice? ☐

C I've seen the perfect suit on sale in my favourite shop and it's exactly what I'm looking for. The only problem is it's an M and I'm an L. What do you think I should do? ☐

D I really like one of my colleagues at work, and I think she likes me, too. I'd really like to go out with her, but I don't know how to ask her. Any advice? ☐

E I have three children and they all have terrible problems with their teeth. We're always at the dentist's and each visit costs a lot of money. Any advice? ☐

F I've always been very nervous, but now it's getting worse. I don't have time to eat at work, so I have five or six coffee breaks during the day. What should I do? ☐

G I've had an argument with my girlfriend, and I don't know what to do. I feel very stupid and I really want to see her again. What do you think I should do? ☐

2 VOCABULARY get

Complete the sentences with the correct form of *get* and a word from the box.

~~divorced~~ fit home lost text message on school
tickets worse up

---

1 Her parents aren't happy together, so they're going to ___*get*___ ___*divorced*___ .
2 Are your children in bed when your husband _____ _____ from work?
3 Our satnav wasn't working and we _____ _____ on the way to our friends' house.
4 I'm going to the gym because I want to _____ _____.
5 The pain in my neck was _____ _____, so I went to the doctor.
6 This morning I _____ _____ for the concert online. They're very good ones at the front!
7 How well do you _____ _____ with your brothers and sisters?
8 I've just _____ a _____ from my boyfriend saying he's going to be late.
9 I don't feel like _____ _____ today. I'm going to stay in bed.
10 I often _____ to _____ late, although it's very near where I live.

3 PRONUNCIATION /ʊ/ and /uː/

a (Circle) the word with a different sound.

ʊ bull	1	pull	(food)	would
uː boot	2	could	you	soon
ʊ bull	3	woman	wouldn't	soup
uː boot	4	book	do	two

b ◖8.1 Listen and check. Then listen again and repeat the words.

4 LISTENING

a ◖8.2 Listen to five speakers talking about a person they discuss their problems with. How many of them talk to members of their family?

b Listen again and match the speakers with the sentences A–E.

Speaker 1 ___*C*___
Speaker 2 ___
Speaker 3 ___
Speaker 4 ___
Speaker 5 ___

A has had some similar experiences to this person.
B also gives advice to this person.
~~C is in a relationship with someone he/she met through this person.~~
D doesn't always agree with this person.
E first met this person when he/she was very young.

USEFUL WORDS AND PHRASES

Learn these words and phrases.

attend (a conference) /əˈtend/
risk (verb) /rɪsk/
macho /ˈmætʃəʊ/
instead /ɪnˈsted/
avoid somebody /əˈvɔɪd sʌmbədi/
be worth (doing) /bi wɜːθ/
change your mind /tʃeɪndʒ jɔː maɪnd/
go for (sth) /gəʊ fɔː/
keep in touch (with sbd) /kiːp ɪn tʌtʃ/

If everything seems to be going well, you have obviously overlooked something.

Murphy's Law

8B If something can go wrong...

1 GRAMMAR *if* + present, + *will* + infinitive (first conditional)

a Match the sentence halves.

Here are six more examples of Murphy's Law:

1 If you lose something,   `c`
2 If you arrive early at a party,   ☐
3 If you make an appointment with the doctor,   ☐
4 If you don't do your homework,   ☐
5 If you buy a new carpet,   ☐
6 If you get into a hot bath,   ☐

a you'll feel better before you see him.
b you'll drop something on it the first day.
c ~~you'll find it in the last place you look.~~
d the phone will ring.
e everyone else will be late.
f your teacher will ask you for it.

b Circle the correct form.

1 If the plane arrives late tonight, I **will miss** / **miss** the last bus.
2 If you **see** / **will see** an accident, call the police!
3 They won't get lost, if they **use** / **will use** their satnav.
4 We **don't get** / **won't get** to the cinema in time if we don't leave now.
5 If you **don't take** / **won't take** an umbrella, it'll definitely rain!
6 If my phone **doesn't work** / **won't work** here, can I use yours?
7 Kathy **is** / **will be** disappointed if she doesn't get the job.
8 If there **isn't** / **won't be** much traffic when we leave, it won't take long to get there.

c Complete the texts with the correct form of the verb in brackets. Then read and match the texts with the correct pictures, A–G.

Traditions and Superstitions

1 Giving a knife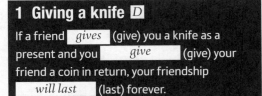
If a friend *gives* (give) you a knife as a present and you *give* (give) your friend a coin in return, your friendship *will last* (last) forever.

2 Horseshoe ☐
If you _____ (hang) a horseshoe above your door, it _____ (bring) good luck to you and your family.

3 Ladders ☐
If you _____ (walk) under a ladder, you _____ (have) bad luck.

4 Throwing a coin in a fountain ☐
If you _____ (throw) a coin into a well or fountain and _____ (make) a wish, the wish _____ (come) true.

5 Falling leaves ☐
If it _____ (be) the first day of autumn, and you _____ (catch) a falling leaf, you _____ (not be) ill all winter.

6 Mirrors ☐
If you _____ (break) a mirror, you _____ (have) seven years bad luck.

7 Spiders ☐
If you _____ (see) a spider on its web, watch it carefully. If the spider _____ (run) down the web, you _____ (go) on a trip soon.

2 VOCABULARY confusing verbs

Complete the sentences with the correct verbs in the correct tense.

1 **look, look like**

You ___look___ very smart in that suit. In fact, you ___look like___ a businessman!

2 **lose, miss**

I _____ my ticket, so I _____ the train and I was late for work.

3 **say, tell**

My son doesn't often _____ lies, but if he does, he always _____ sorry.

4 **hope, wait**

I'm _____ for the bus. I _____ it'll come soon because it's raining.

5 **look at, watch**

Our friends enjoyed _____ the video of our wedding, but they didn't want to _____ the photos of our honeymoon.

6 **know, meet**

She's _____ him since the summer. She _____ him on a safari.

7 **borrow, lend**

If you need to _____ some money, I can _____ you 50 euros.

8 **find, look for**

We were _____ a cheap apartment on the internet and we _____ the perfect place.

9 **carry, wear**

He was _____ a big coat and _____ a heavy suitcase.

10 **bring, take**

I'll _____ you to the airport if you _____ me back a souvenir.

3 PRONUNCIATION linking

a 🔊 8.3 Listen to how the words are linked in each sentence.

1 If I walk, I'll arrive late.
2 It'll be hot if you go in August.
3 If it rains, I'll get a taxi.
4 She'll get angry if we don't invite her.
5 If we get up early, we can go to the market.
6 If I don't understand the menu, I'll ask the waiter.

b Listen again. Practise saying the sentences.

4 LISTENING

a 🔊 8.4 Listen to a radio programme about natural disasters. How many tips does the expert give?

b Listen again and answer the questions.

1 Can you avoid natural disasters? ___No, you can't.___
2 At what time of year should you not go to the Caribbean? _____
3 What will travel insurance probably pay for? _____
4 Why is it important not to panic? _____
5 Who should you contact as soon as possible? _____
6 What should you ask your airline when you book your flight? _____

USEFUL WORDS AND PHRASES

Learn these words and phrases.

blizzard /'blɪzəd/
cyclone /'saɪkləʊn/
earthquake /'ɜːθkweɪk/
flood /flʌd/
forest fire /'fɒrɪst faɪə/
monsoon /mɒn'suːn/
tsunami /tsuː'nɑːmi/
spill (coffee) /spɪl/
parking space /'pɑːkɪŋ speɪs/
natural disaster /'nætʃrəl dɪ'zɑːstə/

8C You must be mine

1 GRAMMAR possessive pronouns

a Complete the questions and answers in the chart.

Whose...?	Possessive adjective	Possessive pronoun
1 *Whose bag is that?*	It's my bag.	It's *mine* _____.
2 *Whose books are those?*	They're your books.	They're _____.
3 _____	It's his laptop.	It's _____.
4 _____	They're her keys.	They're _____.
5 _____	It's our car.	It's _____.
6 _____	They're your coats.	They're _____.
7 _____	It's their house.	It's _____.

b Complete the sentences with a possessive adjective (*my*, *your*, etc.) or pronoun (*mine*, *yours*, etc.)..

1 **A** Are those __*my*__ glasses?
 B No, they're __*his*__ . __*Yours*__ are in your pocket!

2 **A** Whose coats are these? Are they _____?
 B Yes, they're _____. Thanks a lot.

3 **A** Is that your boyfriend's car? It looks like _____.
 B No, it isn't. _____ car is bigger than that.

4 **A** Whose cat is that? It isn't _____.
 B I've seen it in the neighbours' garden. I think it's _____.

5 **A** Is that a new phone? _____ old one was black.
 B No, it's my sister's. _____ is broken, so I'm borrowing _____.

2 VOCABULARY
adverbs of manner

Make adverbs from the adjectives in the box and complete the sentences.

calm dream lazy quiet serious ~~slow~~

1 Please walk more __*slowly*__ . You're going too fast!
2 Sorry? I can't hear you. You're speaking very _____.
3 Mary hardly ever laughs. She takes things really _____.
4 'I don't feel like doing anything today,' he said _____.
5 'I'd love to retire early and live on a tropical island,' Mark said _____.
6 Although all the passengers were worried, the flight attendant spoke _____ and explained the problem.

3 PRONUNCIATION
word stress

a Under<u>line</u> the stressed syllable.

1 de|tec|tive
2 dis|tance
3 do|llar
4 ad|van|tage
5 en|joy
6 com|plete|ly
7 re|mem|ber
8 pro|mise
9 sus|pi|cious

b 🔊 8.5 Listen and check. Then listen again and repeat the words.

4 READING

a Read the article about five famous British chefs. Do you recognize any of them?

Heston Blumenthal is an English chef who is famous for preparing food scientifically. After finishing secondary school, Heston went to France and taught himself to cook. He now owns the Fat Duck Restaurant in Bray, Berkshire, UK, which has three Michelin stars and has twice been voted Best Restaurant in the UK. He has had a number of TV shows and has also published several books.

Delia Smith is one of Britain's oldest cooks and she's the UK's best-selling cookery author. She started her career as a hairdresser at 16, but changed to cooking when she was 21. For 12 years, she wrote about cooking and famous chefs around the world before her first television appearance. She eventually had her own programme, where she explained carefully to viewers how to make basic dishes for the whole family.

Jamie Oliver is one of Britain's best-loved television chefs. His programmes have been broadcast internationally in countries like the USA, South Africa, Australia, Brazil, Japan, and Iceland, and his books have been translated into thirty languages. Jamie is most famous for his campaigns to encourage British and American schoolchildren to eat healthily. He's married with four children.

Nigella Lawson is a popular food writer and journalist who started work as a book reviewer and restaurant critic. She has always been interested in food and cookery, but she has never trained as a cook. Despite this, she has successfully hosted her own cooking shows on TV, especially in the USA, where she had almost two million viewers. She also has her own range of products called *Living Kitchen*.

Gordon Ramsay is one of Britain's top chefs and he has won sixteen Michelin stars in total. He owns restaurants all over the world, but he also helps other restaurant owners who are having problems with their business. Gordon is probably most famous as the host of the TV reality show *Hell's Kitchen*, where he often shouted angrily at the participants when they made a mistake.

b Read the article again and answer the questions. Write H, D, J, N, or G.

Who…?

1 ate in restaurants and read books in his / her first job   _N_
2 isn't very patient with people who are learning to cook   __
3 had a completely different job when he / she left school   __
4 uses chemistry in his / her cooking   __
5 thinks young people should eat better   __

c <u>Underline</u> five words you don't know. Use your dictionary to look up their meaning and pronunciation.

5 LISTENING

a 🔊 8.6 Listen to a conversation about an experiment on a TV programme. Which question did the experiment hope to answer? Was it successful?

b Listen again. Mark the sentences T (true) or F (false).

1 The programme was on in the evening.   _T_
2 There were three cooks.   __
3 The rules for each course were that they had to use the same ingredients.   __
4 There were two judges.   __
5 The cooks were professional restaurant critics.   __
6 Ewan only remembers two dishes because the judges found it very difficult to decide who made them.   __

USEFUL WORDS AND PHRASES

Learn these words and phrases.

advantage /əd'vɑːntɪdʒ/
expenses /ɪk'spensɪz/
exclaim /ɪk'skleɪm/
trust /trʌst/
suspicious /sə'spɪʃəs/
calmly /'kɑːmli/
dreamily /'driːmɪli/
masterfully /'mɑːstəfəli/
the suburbs /ðə 'sʌbɜːbz/
somebody else /'sʌmbədi els/

All animals are equal – but some animals
are more equal than others.
From Animal Farm *by George Orwell, British writer*

9A What would you do?

1 GRAMMAR *if* + past, *would* + infinitive (second conditional)

a Match the sentence beginnings and endings.

1 If my sister were older,   [f]   a   if he could swim.
2 My parents would buy a bigger house   [ ]   b   you'd be really scared.
3 He'd go sailing   [ ]   c   if they couldn't watch TV?
4 What would people do   [ ]   d   if it wasn't raining.
5 If you saw that horror film,   [ ]   e   if they had more money.
6 I'd go for a walk   [ ]   f   ~~she could go to the party with me.~~

b Order the words to complete the sentences and questions.

1 car / would / I / it / to / work / drive / a / had
   If I   *had a car, I would drive it to work* .
2 you / found / do / a / you / million / would / if / euros
   What _____?
3 if / he / could / a / afford / one / phone
   He'd buy _____.
4 caviar / it / I / eat / gave / me / wouldn't
   If someone _____.
5 say / could / talk / if / to / you / the / would / president / you
   What _____?
6 job / for / you / a / I / new / if / look / were
   I'd _____.

c Complete the second conditional sentences with the correct form of the verbs in brackets.

1 If a bee *flew* (fly) into my bedroom, I *would open* (open) the window.
2 If my sister _____ (see) a mouse in the kitchen, she _____ (scream).
3 We _____ (not have) a dog if we _____ (not have) a garden.
4 If my brother _____ (not be) allergic to animals, he _____ (get) a cat.
5 If I _____ (live) in the country, I _____ (learn) to ride a horse.
6 What _____ you _____ (do) if a dangerous dog _____ (attack) you?

2 VOCABULARY animals

Complete the crossword.

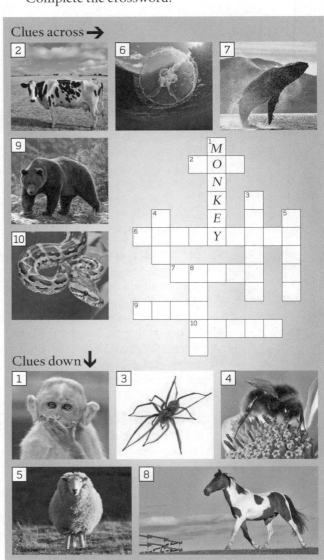

Clues across →

Clues down ↓

3 PRONUNCIATION word stress

a Underline the stressed syllables.

1 but|ter|fly	5 dol|phin	9 li|on	13 spi|der
2 ca|mel	6 el|e|phant	10 mon|key	14 ti|ger
3 chi|cken	7 gi|raffe	11 mos|qui|to	
4 cro|co|dile	8 je|lly|fish	12 ra|bbit	

b 🔊 9.1 Listen and check. Then listen again and repeat the words.

4 READING

a Read the first part of the text and tick (✓) the things you would do.

CROCODILE ATTACK!

If you were swimming at the edge of the water in Southern Florida, USA, and you saw a crocodile coming towards you, what would you do?

'I'd run away fast.'	☐	'I'd pretend to be dead.' ☐
'I'd try to open its mouth.'	☐	'I'd put my fingers into its eyes.' ☐
'I'd make a loud noise.'	☐	'I'd try to fight it.' ☐

b Now read the rest of the article. Which sentence is the best summary?

1 There's nothing you can do if a crocodile attacks you.
2 There are lots of things you can do if a crocodile attacks you.
3 There's only one thing to do if a crocodile attacks you.

Well, most of these are possible – the best thing to do depends on where the crocodile is at the time. If it comes towards you on land, experts say you should turn around and run away as fast as possible. Crocodiles can run faster than humans over a short distance, but they soon get tired. If they miss their first chance to catch their victim, they usually start looking for something else.

If you're in the water, then splash around to make a noise so that the animal gets confused. If this doesn't work, push your thumb or fingers into the crocodile's eye. This is the most sensitive area of the crocodile's body and it is the place where you can cause the animal the most pain . It will also be very surprised by your attack and it's quite possible that it will decide to leave you alone. Don't try and open the crocodile's mouth because the muscles are so strong that this is nearly impossible.

However, if the crocodile is in a bad mood , it's possible that it will carry on fighting. Your final opportunity is to pretend to be dead. If the crocodile thinks that its victim is dead, it opens its mouth for a few seconds to move the body into its throat. This can give you your last chance to escape, but it's a very dangerous plan.

Our final advice? It's much better to avoid crocodiles than to do any of the things above...

c Look at the highlighted words or phrases. Check their meaning and pronunciation with your dictionary.

5 LISTENING

a 🔊 9.2 Listen to a news story about a shark attack. How did the man survive?

_____

b Listen again and answer the questions.

1 Where is Eric Nerhus from?

_____

2 What was he doing when the shark attacked?

_____

3 Which parts of his body were in the shark's mouth?

_____

4 What was Eric's vest made of?

_____

5 Who rescued Eric?

_____

6 How did Eric get to hospital?

_____

7 What injuries did he have?

_____

8 How big was the shark?

_____

USEFUL WORDS AND PHRASES

Learn these words and phrases.

pockets /ˈpɒkɪts/
backwards /ˈbækwədz/
bite /baɪt/
float /fləʊt/
shout /ʃaʊt/
sting /stɪŋ/
suck /sʌk/
tie /taɪ/
wave /weɪv/
keep still /kiːp ˈstɪl/

9B I've been afraid of it for years

1 VOCABULARY phobias and words related to fear

a Complete the phobias with the missing vowels. Then match them with the definitions.

1 *a g o r a p h o b i a*   [b]   a   fear of spiders
2 cl_ _ str_ph_b_ _ _   [ ]   b   fear of open spaces
3 _ r_chn_ph_b_ _ _   [ ]   c   fear of heights
4 gl_ss_ph_b_ _   [ ]   d   fear of closed spaces
5 _cr_ph_b_ _ _   [ ]   e   fear of public speaking

b Complete the sentences with a suitable word.

1 Are you fr*ightened* of snakes? A lot of people are.
2 I'm quite sc_____ of spiders. I don't like them much.
3 If you suffer from a f_____ of flying, you can't travel by plane.
4 My sister is te_____ of big dogs. She always crosses the road if she sees one.
5 My children don't like swimming. They're a_____ of water.
6 Olga has a ph_____ of insects. She never goes to the country.

2 GRAMMAR present perfect + *for* and *since*

a (Circle) the correct word, *for* or *since*, to complete each sentence.

1 Jess hasn't flown on a plane (for)/ since many years.
2 I haven't seen my parents **for** / **since** my birthday.
3 He hasn't ridden a horse **for** / **since** he fell off one when he was twelve.
4 We've had our rabbit **for** / **since** six months.
5 My gran has agoraphobia. She hasn't left the house **for** / **since** two years.
6 I've been afraid of dogs **for** / **since** I was very young.
7 Oliver is ill. He hasn't eaten **for** / **since** two days.
8 We haven't been back there **for** / **since** the accident happened.

b Complete the text with *for* and *since*.

A celebrity's life
Kristen Stewart, actress

Kristen Stewart has been a famous actress [1] __*for*__ about five years now. She has been an actress [2] _____ she was eight years old, when her agent saw her performing at school. Her first role was in a film where she didn't speak, but [3] _____ then she has been in many films. She is probably best known for playing Bella Swan in *The Twilight Saga*, a part which she has played [4] _____ four years.

Kristen has lived in Los Angeles [5] _____ she was born. Because she was acting at a young age, she couldn't go to school, so she studied online. [6] _____ then, she has completed high school. She is now one of the best-paid actresses in Hollywood.

Something many people don't know about Kristen is that she has equinophobia, or a fear of horses. She has had this problem [7] _____ most of her life, but her fans have only known about it [8] _____ 2012, when she was filming with horses. Kristen explained that she has been scared of them [9] _____ she was nine years old, when she had a terrible fall during a horse-riding accident.

c Complete the questions about Kristen Stewart. Use *How long* or *When* and the verb in brackets.

1 <u>When did</u> Kristen Stewart <u>start</u> acting? (start)
   When she was eight.
2 _____ she _____ the part of Bella Swan? (play)
   For four years.
3 _____ Kristen _____ in Los Angeles? (live)
   Since she was born.
4 _____ Kristen _____ equinophobia? (have)
   For most of her life.
5 _____ fans _____ about her phobia? (hear)
   In 2012.

d Right (✓) or wrong (✗)? Correct the mistakes in the **bold** phrases.

1 **Gill hates flying** since she was a child.
   <u>Gill has hated flying</u>_____.
2 **How long time** has your brother been an actor?
   _____?
3 **We've been married** since 2000.
   _____.
4 He's been in the USA **for February**.
   _____.
5 How long **do you have** your dog?
   _____?
6 He's had this job **since eight years**.
   _____.
7 I've had four cars **since I learned to drive**.
   _____.
8 **She's known Sally** since they were at school.
   _____.

3 PRONUNCIATION sentence stress

🔊 9.3 Listen and repeat the sentences. <u>Copy the rhythm.</u>

1 **How long** have you **worked here**?
2 **How long** have they **been <u>married</u>**?
3 **How long** has she **known** him?
4 **We've lived** here for **six months**.
5 I've **<u>studied</u> <u>English</u>** for **three years**.
6 He's had a **<u>phobia</u> since** he was a **child**.

4 LISTENING

a 🔊 9.4 Listen to a radio call-in programme about phobias. What is cynophobia?

b Listen again and choose the correct answers.

1 The caller is worried about…
   a her pet.
   (b) someone in her family.
   c her phobia.
2 The dog bit…
   a the neighbour.
   b the caller.
   c the caller's son.
3 The caller wants some advice about…
   a preventing a phobia.
   b keeping dogs.
   c treating a phobia.
4 The psychologist tells the caller…
   a to keep her son away from dogs.
   b to talk about her son's experience with him.
   c to let her son play with a friend's dog.

USEFUL WORDS AND PHRASES

Learn these words and phrases.

cure /ˈkjʊə/
drug /drʌg/
heights /haɪts/
overcome (a fear) /əʊvəˈkʌm/
panic /ˈpænɪk/
afraid /əˈfreɪd/
frightened /ˈfraɪtnd/
rational (opp *irrational*) /ˈræʃənəl/
scared /skeəd/
terrified /ˈterɪfaɪd/
affect sbd / sth (verb) /əˈfekt/
have an effect on sbd/sth /hæv ən ɪˈfekt ɒn/

9C Born to sing

1 VOCABULARY biographies

Complete the phrases.

1	My grandad was	[c]	a on his 65th birthday.
2	He went	[ ]	b in love with my gran at school.
3	He fell	[ ]	c ~~born in 1945~~.
4	He left	[ ]	d to school when he was five.
5	He started	[ ]	e work when he was 17.
6	They got	[ ]	f school in 1960.
7	They had	[ ]	g three children.
8	He retired	[ ]	h married in 1968.

2 GRAMMAR present perfect or past simple (2)?

a (Circle) the correct verb forms.

My mum was born in Plymouth in 1948. When ¹(she left) / she's
left school, she started work in an office in Plymouth. Later, the
company ²sent / has sent her to a different office in Bristol,
where ³she met / she's met my dad. ⁴They fell / They've fallen
in love, and ⁵they got / they've got married in 1970. ⁶They had /
They've had three children – I'm the youngest.

⁷They moved / They've moved back to Plymouth again when
my dad retired. They bought a very nice house and ⁸they lived /
they've lived there for two years now. My dad ⁹just put /
has just put a greenhouse in the garden for growing vegetables –
¹⁰he was / he's been a keen gardener all his life. My parents
¹¹made / have made a lot of new friends and they're very
happy in their new home.

b Write the verbs in the past simple or present perfect. Use
contractions where necessary.

1 **A** How long ___have___ you ___studied___ English? (study)
 B Since I was little. I ___started___ learning it at school.
 (start)

2 **A** Are Tom and Gill married?
 B Yes, they are.
 A When _____ they _____ married? (get)
 B Last year. But they _____ together for about
 ten years now. (be)

3 **A** Is that man the new accountant?
 B Yes, he is.
 A How long _____ he _____ here? (work)
 B Only for two months. He _____ university in June.
 (finish)

4 **A** How long _____ you _____ your car?
 (have)
 B A long time! I _____ it in 2005, I think. (buy)

5 **A** When _____ Sandra _____ her
 boyfriend? (meet)
 B When she was at university. She _____ him for
 three years now. (know).

6 **A** How long _____ you _____ in London?
 (live)
 B Not long. I _____ six months ago. (arrive)

3 PRONUNCIATION word stress

a Write the words in the correct group.

~~award~~ ~~children~~ divorced married musician primary
retire secondary separate (verb) successful

1 Stress on 1st syllable	2 Stress on 2nd syllable
children	*award*
_____	_____
_____	_____
_____	_____
_____	_____

b 🔊 9.5 Listen and check. Then listen again and
repeat the words.

4 READING

a Read the text about John Lennon. Order the paragraphs 1–7.

John Lennon and his sons

A ☐ On 8 December, 1980, one of John Lennon's fans shot him outside his apartment. Since then, both of his sons have become musicians. Julian Lennon has made six albums and Sean Lennon has sung and played bass guitar with a number of different bands. So far, however, neither of them have been as successful as their father.

B ☐ John Lennon was born in Liverpool on 9 October, 1940. His parents separated when he was five, so he went to live with an aunt and uncle. However, he stayed in contact with his mother, who played him Elvis Presley records and taught him how to play the banjo.

C ☐ Before The Beatles broke up in 1970, John met the Japanese artist, Yoko Ono, and he divorced his first wife. He left the band and continued making music both on his own and with Yoko. Their son, Sean, was born on 9 October, 1975 and John stayed at home to look after him.

D ☐ When John was 15, his mother bought him his first guitar. He formed his first band called The Quarrymen while he was still at school. When he left school, he started a course at Art College, but the band took up a lot of his time, so he didn't finish the course.

E ☐ The band released their first single 'Love Me Do' in October, 1962. They started touring the country. John married his first wife, Cynthia, in secret, and his first son, Julian, was born while they were away. Fans went mad wherever The Beatles played and all of their albums reached the number one spot in the charts.

F ☐ 1 The singer-songwriter and guitarist John Lennon is one of the greatest musicians of all time. Songs like *Give peace a chance* and *Imagine* made him famous all over the world.

G ☐ John met Paul McCartney at the second performance of The Quarrymen and he soon joined the band. Later, George Harrison joined them as lead guitarist. In 1960, they became The Beatles and they started looking for a drummer. Ringo Starr replaced their original drummer, Pete Best, in 1962.

b Circle the correct verb form in the questions.
1 When **was** / **has been** John Lennon born?
2 What **did his mother buy** / **has his mother bought** for him?
3 How long **were** / **have been** The Beatles together?
4 How **did John Lennon die** / **has John Lennon died**?
5 How many albums **did Julian Lennon make** / **has Julian Lennon made**?
6 Which instrument **did Sean Lennon play** / **has Sean Lennon played** with different bands?

c Underline five words you don't know. Use your dictionary to check their meaning and pronunciation.

5 LISTENING

a 🔊 9.6 Listen to a radio programme about the American actress and singer Judy Garland and her daughter, Liza Minnelli. How old were they when they first performed on stage?

b Listen again and mark the sentences T (true) or F (false).

Both women…
1 were born in the USA.   *T*
2 changed their names.   —
3 started performing when they were very young.   —
4 won Oscars.   —
5 sang together at the London Palladium.   —
6 had problems.   —
7 got married more than once.   —
8 had three children.   —

1 VOCABULARY directions

Complete the directions.

> To get to the hotel you need to ¹turn left and go ²str_____ on until you get to
> the roundabout. Go ³r_____ the roundabout and take the third ⁴e_____.
> Then turn right at the traffic ⁵l_____ and ⁶t_____ the second turning on
> the ⁷l_____. The hotel is called The King's Head and it's on the ⁸r_____.

2 ASKING HOW TO GET THERE

Complete the dialogue with the missing sentences.

~~How do I get to SoHo on the subway?~~   OK. Thanks. See you later.
OK. And then?   How many stops is that?
Could you say that again?   Where is it?

A ¹ _How do I get to SoHo on the subway?_
B Go to the subway station at Grand Central – 42nd Street. Take line 6 towards Brooklyn Bridge – City Hall. Get off at Spring Street.
A ² _____
B OK. Take line 6 from Grand Central – 42nd Street to Spring Street.
A ³ _____
B Seven.
A ⁴ _____
B Then you can walk to the restaurant.
A ⁵ _____
B Come out of the subway on Spring Street. Go straight on for about 80 yards and the restaurant is on the right. It's called _Balthazar_.
A ⁶ _____
B And don't get lost.

3 SOCIAL ENGLISH

Complete the dialogue with the words in the box.

don't   feel   long   mean   said   ~~so~~   stay   think

A I'm ¹ _so_ sorry I'm late. I missed the bus.
B But you're always late.
A I ² _____ I'm sorry.
B Why don't you leave home earlier?
A Look, why ³ _____ we order? I'm really hungry.
B No. I don't want to ⁴ _____ here any more.
A OK. Why don't we go for a walk? I can get a burger or something.
B I don't ⁵ _____ like a walk. It's been a ⁶ _____ day and I'm tired.
A Listen. I'll take you home now. And tomorrow I'll make dinner for you at my house. What do you ⁷ _____?
B OK. I suppose that way you can't be late!

4 READING

a Read the article and answer these questions.

1 How far is it from the airport to Manhattan?   _15 miles_
2 How long does it take to drive there outside the rush hour?   _____
3 How much does AirTrain JFK cost for two people one way?   _____
4 How much does a taxi cost for four people?   _____
5 How much do taxis charge per suitcase?   _____
6 What time is the earliest bus to Manhattan?   _____
7 How much is the fare for an adult and a small child?   _____

JFK (John F Kennedy) International Airport is the largest of the three airports serving New York City. It is located in Southeast Queens, about 15 miles (24km) from Manhattan. Travel time to Manhattan by car during rush hour can be over an hour; at other times it's about thirty to forty minutes.

Getting into town from the airport

Although **AIRTRAIN JFK** does not travel directly to Manhattan, it connects passengers to New York's subway and bus networks. The journey costs $7 and takes about an hour, depending on your destination. If you don't mind carrying your own luggage, this is probably your best option.

TAXIS are available outside every terminal in the airport and there's a $45 flat fee to any location in Manhattan. Taxis will take up to four passengers and there is no additional charge for luggage.

NEW YORK AIRPORT SERVICE EXPRESS BUSES run every 15 to 30 minutes from 6.30 a.m. to 11.10 p.m. from each of the airport terminals. The fare is $13, but you can save money by buying round trip tickets online. One free child under 12 is included in the fare. You can choose to get off at Grand Central, Port Authority or Penn Station and the ride takes about an hour.

b Underline five words or phrases you don't know. Use your dictionary to look up their meaning and pronunciation.

10A The mothers of invention

1 VOCABULARY verbs: *invent, discover,* etc.

Complete the sentences with the past participle of the verbs in the box.

base	call	~~design~~	discover	give	invent
open	play	show	use		

1 The London Olympic Stadium was ___designed___ by the architectural company, Populous.

2 The Statue of Liberty was _____ to the people of the USA as a present from the French people.

3 Gold was first _____ in California in 1848.

4 Lemons and sugar are _____ to make lemonade.

5 The game of rugby was first _____ at Rugby School in the UK.

6 The first public movie was _____ to an invited audience in Indiana in 1894.

7 The river that flows through Washington D.C. in the USA is _____ the Potomac.

8 The first games console was _____ by Ralph H. Baer.

9 Heathrow airport's Terminal 5 was _____ by the Queen in 2008.

10 Many characters in Somerset Maugham's books are _____ on real people.

2 GRAMMAR passive

a Order the words to make sentences.

1 discovered / were / Galileo / Saturn's rings / by /
    ___Saturn's rings were discovered by Galileo___ .

2 is / on / of / life / the film *The Iron Lady* / the / based / Margaret Thatcher

_____ .

3 Apple / invented / mobile phones / by / weren't

_____

4 isn't / petrol / lead / in / used / nowadays

_____

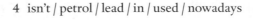

5 sold / low-cost flights / online / are

_____

6 an / were / architect / by / Petronus Towers / designed / the / Argentinian

_____

7 wasn't / Steven Spielberg / *Avatar* / by / directed

_____ .

8 company / by / made / Minis / British / aren't / a / any more

_____ .

b Write sentences in the present or past passive.

1 what / your new baby / call
   What is your new baby called ?

2 contact lenses / invent / a Czech chemist
   _____.

3 where / olives / grow
   _____?

4 the VW Beetle / design / in the 1930s
   _____.

5 diamonds / find / in many different colours
   _____.

6 when / vitamins / discover
   _____?

7 Spanish / speak / in Spain and many parts of
   South America
   _____.

8 where / the _Lord of the Rings_ films / make
   _____?

c Rewrite the sentences in the passive.

1 A factory in China makes these toys.
   These toys _are made by a factory in China_ .

2 People of all ages wear jeans.
   Jeans _____.

3 Microsoft didn't invent laptop computers.
   Laptop computers _____.

4 Does a computer control the heating?
   Is _____?

5 Stieg Larsson wrote _The Millennium Trilogy_.
   The Millennium Trilogy _____.

6 People don't use cassette recorders very much today.
   Cassette recorders _____.

7 Picasso didn't paint _The Scream_.
   The Scream _____.

8 Did the same person direct all the Harry Potter films?
   Were all _____?

3 PRONUNCIATION *-ed*

a 🔊 10.1 Listen and (circle) the past participle with a different *-ed* sound.

1 🐕 **d**og	2 /ɪd/	3 🐕 **d**og	4 /ɪd/	5 👕 **t**ie
call**ed**	check**ed**	open**ed**	rain**ed**	decid**ed**
discover**ed**	invent**ed**	want**ed**	start**ed**	produc**ed**
(paint**ed**)	pretend**ed**	design**ed**	direct**ed**	bas**ed**

b Listen again. Practise saying the words.

4 LISTENING

a 🔊 10.2 Listen to a radio programme about things that have been invented by accident. Match the inventions 1–3 with the inventors a–c.

1 The microwave oven   _b_   a George Crum
2 The X-ray   ☐   b Percy Spencer
3 Crisps   ☐   c Wilhelm Roentgen

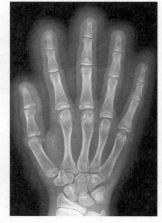

b Listen again and correct the sentences.

1 The discovery that microwaves heated food was made in ~~1954~~. _1945_

2 The microwaves melted a bar of chocolate on the table.

3 The man who discovered the X-ray machine was American.

4 He discovered that electrical rays could pass through water and air.

5 The image on the first X-ray is of the man's hand.

6 Thin fried potatoes are called crisps by Americans.

7 Their inventor was a waiter.

8 The crisps were first called 'Saratoga potatoes'.

USEFUL WORDS AND PHRASES

Learn these words and phrases.

hairdryer /ˈheədraɪə/
hammer /ˈhæmə/
knife /naɪf/
logo /ˈləʊgəʊ/
tin opener /ˈtɪn əʊpnə/
zip /zɪp/
bullet-proof vest /ˈbʊlɪt pruːf vest/
disposable nappies /dɪspəʊzəbl ˈnæpiz/
tinned food /tɪnd fuːd/
windscreen wipers /ˈwɪndskriːn waɪpəz/

The beautiful thing about learning is that
no one can take it away from you.

B B King, American musician

10B Could do better

1 VOCABULARY school subjects

a Match the school subjects and the questions.

1 Foreign languages   [c]
2 Geography   [ ]
3 History   [ ]
4 Literature   [ ]
5 Maths   [ ]
6 Physical Education   [ ]
7 Science   [ ]
8 Information Technology   [ ]
9 Art   [ ]

a What's 15 times 99?
b Who wrote *Macbeth*?
c ~~How do you say 'Thank you' in German?~~
d How do you select a program?
e When did Queen Victoria die?
f How many metres is one lap of an athletics track?
g Who painted *Three Musicians*?
h What's the capital of Sweden?
i What's the chemical symbol for water?

b Match the questions in **a** with the answers.

1 Stockholm   [h]
2 Pablo Picasso   [ ]
3 *Danke schön*   [ ]
4 1,485   [ ]
5 William Shakespeare   [ ]
6 H_2O [ ]
7 400 metres   [ ]
8 Click on the icon.   [ ]
9 1901   [ ]

2 GRAMMAR used to

a Complete the sentences with the correct form of *used to* and the verb phrase.

1 [?] *Did you use to be* (you / be) a good student?
2 [−] I _____ (behave) very well.
3 [+] We _____ (wear) a uniform at school.
4 [?] _____ (Alex / have) a nickname at school?
5 [−] Pupils _____ (not study) IT when I went to school.
6 [+] Her school _____ (be) a same-sex school, but now it's mixed.
7 [−] We _____ (not play) basketball in PE.
8 [?] _____ (your teachers / give) you a lot of homework?

b Correct the mistakes in the highlighted phrases.

1 I use to sit at the back of the class.   *I used to*
2 He used go to school on Saturday mornings.   _____
3 We didn't used to understand our German teacher.   _____
4 Did you used to go to school by bus?   _____
5 School use to start at 9.00 but now it starts at 8.30.   _____
6 Did your friends use help you with your homework?   _____

3 PRONUNCIATION used to / didn't use to

🔊 10.3 Listen and repeat the sentences. Copy the rhythm.

1 I **used** to be **good** at **maths**.
2 **We used** to **hate** the **teacher**.
3 She **didn't use** to **like school**.
4 They **didn't use** to **wear** a **uniform**.
5 **Did** you **use** to play **football** in **PE**?
6 Did **your school** use to **open** in the **holidays**?

4 READING

a Read the interview. Write the questions in the correct place.

Did you have a favourite teacher?

~~Where did you go to school?~~

Did you ever behave badly?

What's the most important lesson you learned at school?

What did you want to do when you left school?

What subjects were you good at?

My schooldays

DAVID SUCHET, actor, played Hercule Poirot in the TV series of Agatha Christie murder mysteries.

Interview by Tim Oglethorpe

1 _Where did you go to school?_

Grenham House, a boarding school in Kent, and Wellington School, a private school in Somerset.

2 _____

One thing my schooldays did teach me was the importance of teamwork. At boarding school, I was an outsider and I was really, truly unhappy there. When I started playing sport at Grenham House, I became a member of a team, and I felt a lot better about myself. Like sport, acting is also nearly always a team event and you rely just as much on other people as they do on you.

3 _____

Yes, I did. My brother and I both went to the same school and sometimes, we used to break the rules. In private schools at that time, a common punishment used to be 'the cane': a long stick which the head teacher used for hitting naughty boys. Both of us were caned on several occasions.

4 _____

Well, I wasn't very academic at all, really, and I was very bad at maths. Luckily for me, I was really good at sport and that's the only reason they accepted me at Wellington. I was in the school rugby team, and I also played tennis. I played at Wimbledon once, in the junior tournament, and I got through to the second round.

5 _____

Although I was good at sport, I never really considered taking it up professionally. Once I left Wellington, I wanted to become an actor and I didn't play nearly as much sport when I left school.

6 _____

Yes, my favourite teacher was Mr Storr, head of the school tennis team, and also my English teacher. One day, when I was 14 or 15, I had to read in class. After the class, he said to me, 'The way you read suggests you might enjoy acting. Would you consider playing Macbeth in the school play?' That was the beginning of my acting career, and I've never looked back since.

b Read the interview again. Mark the sentences T (true) or F (false).

1 He thinks it's important to work together with others. _T_

2 David didn't always enjoy his first school. ___

3 David wanted to be a tennis player when he left school. ___

4 He and his brother used to behave well. ___

5 In the past, the headmaster could hit pupils with a stick. ___

6 David didn't use to be a very good student. ___

7 He only got into Wellington because he was good at sport. ___

8 Mr Storr taught maths and coached the tennis team. ___

c Look at the highlighted words. Use your dictionary to look up their meaning and pronunciation.

5 LISTENING

a ◻ 10.4 Listen to two people talking about language learning in schools. Were Tony and Amy good at languages when they were at school?

_____

b Listen again and (circle) the correct answer.

1 Amy studied (**German**) / **French** the longest.

2 Amy can remember one language more than the others because she **practised it on holiday** / **studied it at university**.

3 Adults remember **some numbers** / **some adjectives** from their language classes.

4 According to the article, some people are **too busy** / **too uncomfortable** to speak a foreign language.

5 **German** / **Italian** is more popular than Spanish.

6 In the future, schools will **offer more European languages** / **make younger pupils learn languages**.

USEFUL WORDS AND PHRASES

Learn these words and phrases.

behaviour /bɪˈheɪvjə/

marks /mɑːks/

nickname /ˈnɪkneɪm/

disorganized /dɪsˈɔːgənaɪzd/

emotional /ɪˈməʊʃənl/

primary school /ˈpraɪməri skuːl/

secondary school /ˈsekəndri skuːl/

express yourself /ɪkˈspres jɔːself/

be good (bad) at /bi ˈɡʊd æt/

The first step to getting what you want out
of life is this: Decide what you want.

Ben Stein, American writer

10C Mr Indecisive

1 GRAMMAR *might* (possibility)

a Max and Sam are telling a colleague about their plans
for next weekend. Complete the text with *might* and a
verb from the box.

~~be~~ eat go have invite make rain take

'We feel like doing something special next weekend, but
we haven't decided what to do yet. It [1] _might be_ sunny,
so we [2] _____ for a walk in the
country on Saturday. We [3] _____
lunch in a restaurant, or we [4] _____
some sandwiches with us.

On the other hand, it [5] _____,
so we won't be able to go out. In that case, we
[6] _____ some friends for dinner
on Saturday. We [7] _____ dinner
ourselves, or we [8] _____ out, we're
not sure.
Everything depends on the weather, really.'

b Complete the sentences with *might* or *might not* and a
verb from the box.

be come fail get go ~~go out~~ have miss

1 I'm really tired so I _might not go out_ tonight.
2 Miguel doesn't speak English, so he _____
the job with the American company.
3 If you have a temperature, you _____ flu.
4 My parents _____ to our party – they're
thinking of going on holiday then.
5 I haven't seen Johnny with Vanessa for a long time.
They _____ together any more.
6 If the taxi doesn't come soon, we _____
the train.
7 We love skiing, so we _____ to the Alps
for our next holiday.
8 Sue hasn't practised much so she _____
her driving test.

2 VOCABULARY word building: noun formation

a Complete the chart with the correct noun or verb.

Verb	Noun
[1] *choose*	choice
confuse	[2] *confusion*
decide	[3]
[4]	death
educate	[5]
[6]	election
imagine	[7]
[8]	information
invite	[9]
[10]	life
opt	[11]
[12]	organization
[13]	success

b Complete the sentences with verbs or nouns from **a**.

1 After the _death_ of my grandfather, my
grandmother came to live with us.
2 I made the right _____ to continue
studying when I left school. I loved university.
3 They're going to _____ all their friends
to their party.
4 _____ at school depends on how hard
you work.
5 We're sorry to _____ passengers that the
14.30 train to Birmingham is delayed.
6 He _____ to study history instead
of geography at school.
7 Can you _____ a world without
electricity?
8 The documentary was about the _____
of the author, Charles Dickens.

3 PRONUNCIATION diphthongs

a Tick (✓) the pairs of words which have the same sound and cross (✗) the pairs that don't.

1	m**igh**t	sc**ie**nce	✓
2	m**ay**	f**ai**l	__
3	kn**ow**	n**ow**	__
4	wh**ere**	w**ere**	__
5	h**ere**	th**ere**	__
6	t**ou**rist	**Eu**rope	__
7	sh**ow**	c**ow**	__
8	n**oi**sy	b**oy**	__

b ◉ 10.5 Listen and check. Then listen again and repeat.

4 READING

a Read the text. What was the aim of the experiment?

b Read the text again and circle the correct answer.

1 The participants in the experiment were all **at university** / **at work**.

2 The two groups were shown the card game **in different places** / **at different times**.

3 The participants had to go back **some time later** / **the next day**.

4 **Some** / **All** of the participants went to bed between the two visits.

5 There were **two** / **four** packs of cards in the card game.

6 The cards in the packs were **the same** / **different**.

7 The group who were taught in the morning **won** / **lost** more often than the other group.

8 The experiment helped researchers find a connection between **being creative** / **REM sleep** and making decisions.

c Highlight five words you don't know. Use your dictionary to look up their meaning and pronunciation.

Let me sleep on it

For many years, people have said that a good night's sleep often helps when you have to make an important decision. Research done recently by an American University has shown that this idea is actually true.

The researchers used a card game for their experiment and 54 students between the ages of 18 and 23 took part. The scientists divided the participants into two groups. Both groups were given a short lesson in how to play the card game, either in the morning or in the evening. The lesson was very short, not long enough for either group to learn exactly how the card game worked. All of the students were asked to come back 12 hours later. The 28 students who had the class in the afternoon went home to a normal evening and their usual night of sleep, while the 26 who received the class in the morning came back after a day of normal activities without having a sleep.

On their second visit, the students played the game for long enough to learn that taking cards from the four different packs gave different results. Two of the packs had cards which helped players win more often while the other two packs had cards which made them lose. The object was to avoid losing the game.

In the experiment, the students who had had a normal night's sleep chose cards from the winning packs four times more than those who had spent the 12-hour break awake. The students who had slept also understood better how to play the game.

These results show that sleep helps a person make better decisions. The researchers think that this has something to do with rapid-eye-movement or REM sleep, which is the creative period of our sleep cycle. The experiment shows that there is a connection between REM sleep and decision making, but researchers do not yet know what the connection is.

5 LISTENING

a ◉ 10.6 Listen to five speakers talking about decisions they have made. How many of them made good decisions?

b Listen again and match the speakers with the sentences.

Speaker 1 __C__ A He / She thought time was more important than money.
Speaker 2 ___ B He / She didn't get a prize.
Speaker 3 ___ C He / She didn't arrive on time.
Speaker 4 ___ D He / She didn't enjoy a special occasion.
Speaker 5 ___ E He / She didn't accept an invitation.

USEFUL WORDS AND PHRASES

Learn these words and phrases.

products /ˈprɒdʌkts/
dissatisfied /dɪsˈsætɪsfaɪd/
indecisive /ɪndɪˈsaɪsɪv/
electrical gadgets
　/ɪlektrɪkl ˈgædʒɪts/
be able to /bi ˈeɪbl tə/

make a decision /ˈmeɪk ə dɪˈsɪʒn/
miss an opportunity /ˈmɪs æn ɒpəˈtjuːnəti/
pick somebody up (= in a car) /ˈpɪk sʌmbədi ʌp/
pick sth /ˈpɪk/
take sth seriously /teɪk ˈsɪəriəsli/

11A Bad losers

1 VOCABULARY sports, expressing movement

a Complete the sentences.

1 The player took two shots to hit the golf ball into the h*ole*.
2 In athletics, the runners run round a tr_____.
3 It was m_____ p_____, and everyone was very tense, but his first s_____ went into the net.
4 The golf player had to try and hit the ball out of the b_____.
5 The athletes were running fast towards the finishing line because they were on the last l_____.
6 When you take a p_____, you have to kick the ball past the goalkeeper.
7 The player who took the c_____ kicked the ball to a team mate, who headed it into the goal.

b <u>Underline</u> the prepositions of movement in **a**.

c Complete the crossword.

Clues across →

2 GRAMMAR expressing movement

a Look at the pictures. Complete the sentences with the past simple of the verbs and the correct preposition.

~~cycle~~   go   hit   kick   run   throw
across   into   over   through   under   ~~up~~

1 They _*cycled*_ _*up*_ the hill.
2 The boy _____ the ball _____ the car.
3 The train _____ _____ the tunnel.
4 He _____ the ball _____ the goal.
5 The children _____ _____ the road.
6 She _____ the ball _____ the net.

Clues down ↓

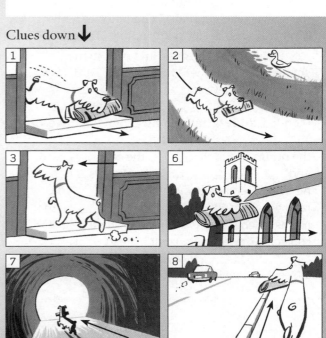

b Look at the picture, read the story, and complete it with the prepositions in the box.

across into out of past ~~round~~ through to
towards under along (x 2)

Last day at school for boy with dirty shoes!

Last Wednesday started as normal for 15-year-old Michael Brewster at Hove Park School.

At 10.30 a.m., Michael's class were jogging
¹ _round_ the gym. But when Charles Duff, the sports teacher, told Michael to clean his dirty trainers, he got really angry. He ran
² _____ the gym, and back to the changing rooms where he found Mr Duff's keys. From there, he went ³ _____ the car park, got ⁴ _____ Mr Duff's Ford Mondeo, and started the car. Then he drove
⁵ _____ the road, ⁶ _____
the bridge, ⁷ _____ the security guard, and ⁸ _____ the school gates. Then he turned left and drove ⁹ _____ the road for about 100 metres ¹⁰ _____ the maths teacher's house. That was when he lost control. He tried to stop, but instead went
¹¹ _____ a field and crashed into a tree. Michael has now left Hove Park School.

3 PRONUNCIATION sports

a Look at the phonetics and write the sport.

1 /ˈfʊtbɔːl/   _football_
2 /ˈvɒlibɔːl/   _____
3 /ˈməʊtə ˈreɪsɪŋ/   _____
4 /ˈskiːɪŋ/   _____
5 /ˈwɪndsɜːfɪŋ/   _____
6 /ˈsaɪklɪŋ/   _____
7 /ˈbɑːskɪtbɔːl/   _____
8 /ˈrʌgbi/   _____
9 /æθˈletɪks/   _____

b ◉ **11.1** Listen and check. Then listen again and repeat the words.

4 LISTENING

a ◉ **11.2** Listen to five people talking about bad losers. Which games or sports do they mention?

_____

b Listen again. Who…?

1 lost a friend after playing sport with him / her   _Speaker 2_
2 is in a team with someone who's a bad loser   _____
3 has a parent who is a bad loser   _____
4 used to let one of their children win   _____
5 has a colleague who is a fanatical sports fan   _____

USEFUL WORDS AND PHRASES

Learn these words and phrases.

coach /kəʊtʃ/
corner /ˈkɔːnə/
hole /həʊl/
lap /læp/
penalty /ˈpenəlti/
beat /biːt/
crash /kræʃ/
race /reɪs/
referee /refəˈriː/
score a goal /ˈskɔː(r) ə gəʊl/

11B Are you a morning person?

1 VOCABULARY phrasal verbs

a Complete what the people are saying in each picture.

1 Turn __*down*__ the radio! It's very loud!
2 Don't worry! The match will be _____ soon.
3 We need someone who can look _____ our dog while we're on holiday.
4 Take _____ your shoes before you come in!
5 Can you fill _____ this form, please?
6 Put _____ a different jacket! That one looks awful!

b Complete the sentences with the verbs in the box.

~~find out~~   get on with   give up   go out   look forward to   look up
take back   throw away   try on   turn up
---

1 Chris called the station to __*find out*__ the times of the trains.
2 I never _____ empty jam jars. I wash them and then re-use them.
3 It's very cold in here. Can you _____ the heating?
4 The teacher told us to _____ the words we didn't understand.
5 We love travelling, so we always _____ our holidays.
6 I don't really like my sister's new boyfriend. I don't _____ him at all.
7 They only _____ on Friday or Saturday nights because they start work early during the week.
8 It's best to _____ clothes before you buy them.
9 We're going to _____ our new coffee machine because it doesn't work properly.
10 Anna's going to _____ sweets and chocolate for a month to try to lose weight.

2 GRAMMAR word order of phrasal verbs

a (Circle) the correct phrases. If both are possible, tick (✓) the sentence.

1 Please **turn off the lights** / **turn the lights off** before you go to bed. ✓
2 Thanks for the money. I'll **pay it back** / **pay back it** tomorrow.
3 I can't find my keys. Can you help me **look for them** / **look them for**?
4 Why don't you **try on that dress** / **try that dress on**? I think it'll suit you.
5 My mum usually **looks after my kids** / **looks my kids after** when we go out.
6 If you've finished playing, please **put the toys away** / **put away the toys**.

b Rewrite the sentences with a pronoun. Change the word order if necessary.

1 Can you write down **your email address**?
   __*Can you write it down*_____?
2 She'll give back **the exams** on Friday.
   _____.
3 Are you looking forward to **your party**?
   _____?
4 I called back **my mother** when I got home.
   _____.
5 We don't get on with **our new neighbours**.
   _____.
6 Shall we turn on **the TV**?
   _____?

3 PRONUNCIATION linking

🔊 11.3 Listen and repeat the sentences. Try to link the words.

1 Throw it away!
2 Turn it up!
3 Write it down!
4 Put it away!
5 Give it back!
6 Fill it in!

71

4 READING

a Read the article. Complete the gaps with these phrasal verbs.

| ~~find out~~ get up give up go out put on take off |
| turn on write down |

b Read the article again. Tick (✓) the people with good habits and cross (✗) the bad ones.

1 I go to bed every night at 11 o'clock.
2 I sleep for six hours during the week and ten hours at the weekend.
3 I always have lunch at my desk to save time.
4 I always wear sunglasses.
5 My bedroom is sometimes too cold.
6 I sometimes watch a film to help me to go to sleep.
7 I usually have dinner at 7.30 p.m.
8 I often have a cup of coffee before I go to bed.
9 I keep a notebook by the side of my bed.
10 I sometimes meditate if I can't sleep.

c Look at the highlighted words or phrases and guess their meaning. Use your dictionary to look up their meaning and pronunciation.

5 LISTENING

a 🔊 11.4 Listen to an interview with Graham, a taxi driver who usually works at night. Is he positive or negative about his job?

b Listen again. Mark the sentences T (true) or F (false).

1 Graham goes to sleep immediately after getting home from work.   _F_
2 The first meal he has when he gets up is lunch. __
3 His children wake him up at about three o'clock. __
4 He never feels tired when he wakes up. __
5 He eats three times a day. __
6 He doesn't mind his working hours. __

USEFUL WORDS AND PHRASES

Learn these words and phrases.

buzz /bʌz/
energetic /enəˈdʒetɪk/
live (adjective) /laɪv/
sleepy /ˈsliːpi/
wild (night) /waɪld/
bowl (of cereal) /ˈbəʊl/
any time /ˈeni taɪm/
social life /ˈsəʊʃl laɪf/
set (your alarm clock) /set/
stay in bed /ˈsteɪ ɪn bed/

Still tired in the morning?

Five tips for getting a better night's sleep

Sleep at the same times

¹ _Find out_ how much sleep you need and make sure that you get it. Go to bed and ² _____ at the same time each day and you will have more energy than if you sleep the same number of hours at different times.

Make sure you are exposed to light during the day

Your body needs natural light to produce the hormone melatonin, which regulates your sleeping and waking cycle. Don't stay inside all day – ³ _____ in your lunch break , for example for a short walk. On a sunny day ⁴ _____ your sunglasses for at least half an hour to let light onto your face.

Create a relaxing routine before going to bed

Have a hot bath. Then ⁵ _____ your pyjamas and make sure your bedroom is at the right temperature. Don't watch TV in bed, as it will stimulate rather than relax you.

Avoid stimulants

Don't eat big meals or drink coffee late at night. Avoid drinking alcohol before you go to bed and ⁶ _____ smoking! Cigarettes can cause a number of sleep problems.

Getting back to sleep

If you wake up in the middle of the night and can't get back to sleep, try a relaxation technique like meditation. If that doesn't work, ⁷ _____ the light and read a book. If you're worried about something, ⁸ _____ your problem on a piece of paper so that you can deal with it in the morning.

> **If the tips above don't help, you might need to see a sleep doctor.**

11C What a coincidence!

1 GRAMMAR *so, neither* + auxiliaries

a Complete the conversation with the phrases from the box.

~~Neither did I~~   Neither have I   Neither was I
So am I   So do I   So would I

A Hi, Tom. Do you ever watch *Who do you think you are*? You know, that TV series about celebrities who find out about their families?
B Yes, I do. But I didn't see it last night.
A ¹ *Neither did I*. I wasn't at home.
B ² _____. But I usually watch it every week.
B ³ _____. I think it's really interesting. I'd love to find out about my family.
A ⁴ _____. I'm thinking about looking for some information on the internet.
B ⁵ _____. But I haven't done anything about it yet.
A ⁶ _____.

b Respond to the statements with *So* or *Neither*, to say that you are the same.

1 I'm going out tonight.
  So am I _____.
2 I enjoyed the party.
  _____.
3 I haven't done the homework.
  _____.
4 I was late today.
  _____.
5 I'm not hungry.
  _____.
6 I can't drive.
  _____.
7 I'd love to travel round the world.
  _____.
8 I don't have any pets.
  _____.

2 VOCABULARY similarities

Complete the text with the words in the box.

as both identical like neither
~~similar~~ so

People think my best friend Sue and I are sisters, because we're very ¹ *similar*. Sue's from the same town ² _____ me, and we look very ³ _____ each other. We ⁴ _____ like shopping, and we have the same taste in clothes. I usually wear trousers and tops, and ⁵ _____ does Sue. She doesn't like short skirts and ⁶ _____ do I. Once we went to a party together wearing ⁷ _____ clothes!

3 PRONUNCIATION sentence stress, word stress

a 🔊 11.5 Listen to the sentences.

1 **So** did **I**.
2 **So** can **I**.
3 **So** have **I**.
4 **Neither** am **I**.
5 **Neither** do **I**.
6 **Neither** was **I**.

b Listen again and repeat the sentences. <u>Copy</u> the <u>rhythm</u>.

c 🔊 11.6 Listen and under<u>line</u> the stressed syllable. Then listen again and repeat the words.

1 i|den|ti|cal
2 si|mi|lar
3 co|in|ci|dence
4 a|ma|zing
5 dis|co|ver
6 e|very|where
7 per|son|a|li|ty
8 de|fi|nite|ly

4 READING

a Read the article and choose the best title.

1 A town with a mystery
2 The problems of having twins
3 Why couples have twins

Today, there are two thousand families living in the village of Kodinhi in southern India. Among them, there are 220 sets of twins, which is six times the global average. What makes this even more unusual is that India has one of the lowest birth rates of twins in the world.

Nobody can explain the reason why the village has so many twins. Some people say the cause might be genetic, but local doctor, Dr Sribiju, doesn't think so. He says that there haven't always been twins in Kodinhi – parents suddenly started having them about sixty or seventy years ago. Neither does he believe that a new kind of pollution has caused the twins to be born. In that case, he argues, there would be more twins with malformations. Luckily, most of Kodinhi's twins are born healthy. Dr Sribiju thinks that the twins are born because of something the villagers eat and drink. He wants to discover just what that is, so that he can use it to help other couples who can't have children.

Having twins in this part of India can be a big problem for a family. It's expensive, and it can be dangerous for the mother's health. That's why the villagers of Kodinhi have started a support group. The group is called the Twins and Kin* Association, or TAKA for short. The president of the group is 50-year-old Pullani Bhaskaran, who has twin sons of his own. He wants all the twins in Kodinhi to join the group so that they can help each other. With the 220 pairs of twins in the village and the other people in their families, TAKA currently has 600 members.

Glossary

kin = family member

b Read the article and mark the sentences T (true) or F (false).

1 Parents don't usually have twins in India. _T_
2 A century ago, there used to be more twins in Kodinhi. ___
3 Dr Sribiju thinks that there are a lot of twins because of the pollution in Kodinhi. ___
4 Dr Sribiju thinks that couples who want children could learn from the villagers of Kodinhi. ___
5 It can be a health risk for women in Kodinhi to have twins. ___
6 The President of TAKA has a twin brother. ___

c Look at the highlighted words and phrases and guess their meaning. Use your dictionary to look up their meaning and pronunciation.

5 LISTENING

a 🔊 11.7 Listen to a radio programme about famous twins. Match the twins (1–3) with the headings (a–c).

1 Romulus and Remus _c_   a criminal twins
2 The Kray Brothers ___   b celebrity twins
3 The Olsen Twins ___   c historical twins

b Read the sentences. Listen again and write RR (Romulus and Remus), KB (the Kray Brothers) or OT (the Olsen Twins).

1 Their parents didn't want them. _R R_
2 They were British. ____
3 They're still alive. ____
4 They met some very famous people. ____
5 They had a serious argument. ____
6 They became famous very young. ____

USEFUL WORDS AND PHRASES

Learn these words and phrases.

tastes /teɪsts/
identical twins
  /aɪdentɪkl ˈtwɪnz/
security guard
  /sɪˈkjʊərəti gɑːd/

adopt (a child) /əˈdɒpt/
by coincidence /baɪ kəʊˈɪnsɪdəns/
great to meet you /greɪt tə ˈmiːt ju/
go to college (AmE) /gəʊ tə ˈkɒlɪdʒ/
look exactly like /lʊk ɪgˈzæktli laɪk/

1 ON THE PHONE

Complete the dialogues.

1 **A** Hello, can I s<u>peak</u> to Oliver, please?
   B T<u>his</u> is Oliver.
   A Hi Oliver, this is Mark. I'm r<u>eturning</u> your call.

2 **A** Hi Amy.
   B I'm s_____, you have the
      wr_____ number.

3 **A** Hello, this is reception. How can I help you?
   B Good morning. Mr Clarke, please.
   A I'm sorry, the l_____ is b_____.
   B OK, can I l_____ a m_____?
   A Yes, of course.
   B Can you tell him Fiona called? I'll c_____
      b_____ later.

4 **A** Good morning, London 24seven.
   B Hello, can I speak to Alison, please?
   A Just a second, I'll p_____ you through.

2 SOCIAL ENGLISH

(Circle) the correct word or phrase.

1 **A** Does your girlfriend know you're here?
   B No, I'll (call her) / call to her now.

2 **A** I've got a new job!
   B That's **great news** / **a great news**.

3 **A** I've got something to tell you.
   B Me, too. But you **do first** / **go first**.

4 **A** What are you doing here?
   B I'll explain **after** / **later**.

5 **A** Is everything alright?
   B **Never better** / **Ever better**.

3 READING

a Read the text. Which sentence is the best summary?

1 British and American English are almost exactly the same.
2 The most important difference between British and American English is the vocabulary.
3 Travellers don't have problems understanding British and American English.

British and American English

If you've learned British English and you're travelling in the States, or if you've learned American English and you're travelling in Britain, you'll notice some differences. An obvious difference is the accent, but most travellers find that they don't have too many problems with this. There are some grammatical differences, but they shouldn't make it difficult to understand people, or to communicate. That leaves differences in vocabulary, which can cause misunderstandings. Sometimes the difference is only the spelling, for example, in British English *centre*, *colour*, and *travelled*, and in American English *center*, *color*, and *traveled*. But sometimes the word is completely different in British and American English, so it's a good idea to be prepared.

b Match the British English with the American English.

British		American
1 bill	c	a cab
2 chips		b cell phone
3 chemist's		c ~~check~~
4 ground floor		d elevator
5 lift		e first floor
6 mobile		f fries
7 petrol		g line
8 queue		h the subway
9 toilet		i pharmacy
10 shop		j rest room
11 taxi		k store
12 trainers		l sneakers
13 the underground		m gas

c <u>Underline</u> five words or phrases you don't know. Use your dictionary to look up their meaning and pronunciation. Make sure you can say them in British and American English.

12A Strange but true!

1 GRAMMAR past perfect

a Complete the sentences with the past perfect form of the verbs in brackets.

1 The streets were white because it ___had snowed___ the night before. (snow)

2 I suddenly remembered that I _____ the windows before I left the house. (not close)

3 We got to the cinema ten minutes after the film _____. (start)

4 Tina felt nervous because she _____ before. (not fly)

5 Paul lent me the book after he _____ it. (read)

6 They missed the flight because they _____ the announcement. (not hear)

b Write questions in the past perfect.

1 **A** I drove my boyfriend's car this morning.
B you / drive it / before
   ___Had you driven it before___?

2 **A** My friends ate sushi in Japan.
B they / eat sushi / before
   _____?

3 **A** My brother won a gold medal.
B he / win a medal / before
   _____?

4 **A** The children made a cake yesterday.
B they / make a cake / before
   _____?

5 **A** My sister ran in the London marathon last weekend.
B she / run a marathon / before
   _____?

6 **A** We went to Brazil on holiday.
B you / be there / before
   _____?

c Make these two sentences into one. Use the past perfect and the past simple.

1 We bought some souvenirs. Then we went back to the hotel.
After *we had bought some souvenirs, we went back to the hotel*.

2 Max did the ironing. Then he put the clothes away.
After Max _____.

3 They watched the news. Then they turned off the TV.
After _____.

4 I read the book. Then I gave it back.
When _____.

5 Ruth tried on the top. Then she went to the checkout.
After Ruth _____.

6 We had dinner. Then we did the washing up.
After _____.

d Circle the correct verb.

Last week my neighbour was on holiday. One night I [1] **heard** / **had heard** a strange noise in her house. I [2] **opened** / **had opened** the door to have a look, and I found that someone [3] **broke** / **had broken** into the house.

Luckily, he (or she!) [4] **already left** / **had already left** when I got there, and they [5] **didn't steal** / **hadn't stolen** much as far as I could see – just the TV.

I was looking for my mobile yesterday morning, but I couldn't find it. I was sure I [6] **didn't lose** / **hadn't lost** it, because I [7] **saw** / **had seen** it twenty minutes before. Then I realized that I [8] **left** / **had left** it in my trouser pocket, and I [9] **put** / **had put** my trousers in the washing machine!

2 PRONUNCIATION contractions: had / hadn't

a Write the sentences with contractions.

1 He had forgotten it. _He'd forgotten it._
2 We had lost it. _____
3 You had seen her. _____
4 It had been a terrible day. _____
5 I had not sent it. _____
6 She had not done it. _____
7 They had not told me. _____

b 🔊 12.1 Now listen and check. Then listen and repeat the sentences. Copy the rhythm.

3 VOCABULARY verb phrases

Complete the sentences with the past simple or past participle of the verbs in the box.

get on get out of ~~free~~ realize put go on
have leave be belong

1 He was re-arrested 24 hours after he had been
   freed from prison.
2 The check-in clerk _____ my suitcase on
   the belt and gave me my boarding pass.
3 This ring _____ to my mother when she
   was young.
4 She wasn't worried because she had _____
   the baby with her mother.
5 My parents weren't at home because they had
   _____ holiday a few days before.
6 After we had _____ the pool, we sunbathed
   for a while.
7 We went to the beach and _____ a swim.
8 When I got to my class, I _____ that I had
   forgotten my books.
9 He _____ in prison when his son was born.
10 The train left a few minutes after they had
   _____ it.

4 LISTENING

a 🔊 12.2 Listen to four true news stories. Number the pictures in the order you hear the stories.

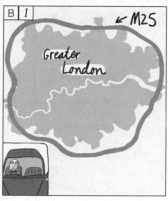

b Listen again and correct the mistakes in the sentences.

1 Dennis Leighton was going to visit his ~~sister~~. _daughter_
2 He had been in his car for 13 hours.
3 Erin Langworthy was on holiday in Kenya.
4 She was taken to hospital after she had walked to safety.
5 Lena Paahlsson lost the ring while she was doing the
   washing up.
6 Today the ring is too big for her.
7 The crocodile had gone into Jo Dodd's kitchen.
8 Mrs Dodd called the Crocodile Management Centre.

USEFUL WORDS AND PHRASES

Learn these words and phrases.

wave /weɪv/	close to (adj) /ˈkləʊs tə/
arrest /əˈrest/	outdoor /ˈaʊtdɔː/
belong /bɪˈlɒŋ/	fortunately /ˈfɔːtʃənətli/
realize /ˈrɪəlaɪz/	net /ˈnet/
steal /stiːl/	rob (a bank) /rɒb/

Gossip is what no one claims to like,
but everybody enjoys.
Joseph Conrad, Polish writer

12B Gossip is good for you

1 GRAMMAR reported speech

a Complete the reported speech.

Direct speech	Reported speech
1 'I want to leave him.'	She said that she ___wanted to leave him___.
2 'I don't like her parents.'	He told me that he _____.
3 'I'm getting divorced.'	She told me that she _____.
4 'I've been to the police station.'	He told me that he _____.
5 'I haven't met his girlfriend.'	She said that she _____.
6 'I saw James with another woman.'	He said that he _____.
7 'I can't cook.'	She told me that she _____.
8 'I won't tell anyone.'	He said that he _____.
9 'I'll speak to her tomorrow.'	She said that she _____.
10 'I've got a lot of work to do.'	He told me that he _____.

b Write the sentences in direct speech.

1 She said she was busy.
   She said: '___I'm busy___.'

2 Jane said that she wanted a cup of coffee.
   She said: '_____.'

3 They told me that they hadn't seen the new neighbours yet.
   They said: '_____.'

4 Steve told me that he didn't want to go to the cinema.
   He said: '_____.'

5 Helen and Paul said they would go to the party.
   They said: '_____.'

6 He said that his computer had just broken.
   He said: '_____.'

7 She told me that the city was very old.
   She said: '_____.'

8 They said that they would visit me.
   They said: '_____.'

2 VOCABULARY say or tell?

a Circle the correct words.

1 Her husband **said** / **told** that he was working late.
2 She **said** / **told** me that she wasn't happy.
3 They **said** / **told** us that they were getting married.
4 You **said** / **told** that she didn't like men with beards.
5 I **said** / **told** you that I had a new girlfriend.
6 We **said** / **told** that we were going to be late.
7 Anna **said** / **told** you that she didn't have a car.
8 I **said** / **told** her that John was busy.
9 He **said** / **told** that we had to do exercise five.
10 You **said** / **told** that she had called Mike this morning.

b Complete the sentences with *said* or *told*.

1 She __said__ that she had been to a friend's house.
2 We _____ our parents we wouldn't be home for lunch.
3 I _____ you that the man wasn't her brother.
4 They _____ that they were going on holiday.
5 He _____ me that he didn't have a girlfriend.
6 You _____ that you weren't going out tonight.
7 James _____ that he was busy tonight.
8 I _____ that the film started at eight o'clock.
9 We _____ them that his sister was on holiday.
10 Olivia _____ me that she had called Jack this morning.

3 PRONUNCIATION double consonants

a Look at the phonetics and write the words.

1 /ˈgɒsɪp/   __gossip__
2 /ˈmærɪd/   _____
3 /ˈletə/   _____
4 /ˈmɪdl/   _____
5 /ˈhʌri/   _____
6 /ˈdɪfrənt/   _____
7 /ˈsɒri/   _____
8 /ˈsʌmə/   _____
9 /ˈmesɪdʒ/   _____
10 /ˈhæpi/   _____

b ◑ 12.3 Listen and check. Then listen again. Practise saying the words.

4 LISTENING

a ◑ 12.4 Listen to Alan and Jess discussing a survey. Do they both gossip at work?

b Listen again and mark the sentences T (true) or F (false).

1 Jess and Alan think that woman gossip more than men.
    _T_
2 According to the results of the survey, Jess and Alan are right.
    —
3 The survey was done by a newspaper.
    —
4 Nobody was surprised by the results of the survey.
    —
5 Over 50 percent of the men in the survey said they gossiped at work.
    —
6 Less than 50 per cent of women said they gossiped at work.
    —
7 The men in the survey talked about topics related to work.
    —
8 The women talked about their male colleagues.
    —

USEFUL WORDS AND PHRASES

Learn these words and phrases.

genes /dʒiːnz/
gossip /ˈgɒsɪp/
share /ʃeə/
according to /əˈkɔːdɪŋ tə/
feel guilty /fiːl ˈgɪlti/
in general /ɪn ˈdʒenrəl/
pass on /ˈpɑːs ɒn/
social skill /ˈsəʊʃl skɪl/

How many roads must a man walk down
before you can call him a man?

Bob Dylan, US singer and songwriter

12C The *English File* quiz

1 GRAMMAR questions without auxiliaries

a Circle the correct question.

1 a Who did paint *The Kiss*?
  b Who painted *The Kiss*?

2 a Which instrument does Angus Young of *AC / DC* play?
  b Which instrument plays Angus Young of *AC / DC*?

3 a How many lives do cats have in the UK?
  b How many lives have cats in the UK?

4 a What did happen in Japan on 11th March 2011?
  b What happened in Japan on 11th March 2011?

5 a Which American singer did die on 25th June 2009?
  b Which American singer died on 25th June 2009?

6 a Who did Beyoncé marry in 2008?
  b Who Beyoncé married in 2008?

7 a What animal caught a train for 50 kms?
  b What animal did catch a train for 50 kms?

8 a What invented Peter Durand in 1810?
  b What did Peter Durand invent in 1810?

b Match the questions in **a** with these answers.

a Nine.   3
b An earthquake and a tsunami.   ___
c Michael Jackson.   ___
d Gustav Klimt.   ___
e Jay-Z.   ___
f Tinned food.   ___
g The guitar.   ___
h A dog.   ___

c Complete the questions for the answers.

1 What _made Mark Zuckerberg_ famous?
  Facebook made Mark Zuckerberg famous.
2 When _____ the football World Cup?
  Spain won the football World Cup in 2010.
3 How long _____ together?
  REM stayed together for 31 years.
4 Who _____ *Jack Sparrow* in *Pirates of the Caribbean*?
  Johnny Depp plays *Jack Sparrow* in *Pirates of the Caribbean*.
5 How _____?
  Amy Winehouse died from alcohol poisoning.
6 Where _____?
  Polar bears live in the Arctic.
7 How many _____ at the Arc de Triomphe in Paris?
  Twelve roads join at the Arc de Triomphe in Paris.
8 Which country _____ in the world?
  India produces the most bananas in the world.

2 VOCABULARY revision

a Circle the word or phrase that is different. Say why it's different.

1	curly	long	slim	straight

It's not used to describe hair.

2	friendly	generous	kind	overweight
3	bracelet	earrings	necklace	tracksuit
4	a course	exercise	a phone call	housework
5	crowded	polluted	dangerous	exciting
6	market	shopping centre	town hall	department store
7	decide	finish	forget	pretend
8	get up	get old	get fit	get lost
9	bee	butterfly	bat	mosquito

b Complete the sentences with **one** word.

1 Why don't you try __on__ that dress?
2 She was born _____ March 24th, 1996.
3 I'll have to take my new top _____ to the shop. It has a hole.
4 Please don't throw _____ my old jeans. I still wear them.
5 You'll have to speak _____ the manager about your complaint.
6 I'm looking _____ to going away at the weekend.
7 The children ran _____ the road without looking. Luckily, there wasn't much traffic.
8 They arrived _____ London at midnight.
9 We carried _____ working until it was time to go home.
10 Can you please pick _____ that rubbish from the floor?

c Complete the missing verbs.

1 go_____ sightseeing
2 s_____ at a campsite
3 f_____ in love with somebody
4 m_____ a mistake
5 d_____ the shopping
6 l_____ money to somebody
7 s_____ hours doing something
8 g_____ on well with somebody
9 e_____ a salary
10 f_____ a job

3 PRONUNCIATION revision

a (Circle) the word with a different sound.

1	æ cat	cap hat (want)
2	ʊ bull	book push school
3	uː boot	lose hope suit
4	ʌ up	turn gloves sunny
5	eɪ train	lazy safe bald
6	əʊ phone	towel goat throw
7	aɪ bike	kind shy thin
8	aʊ owl	cow horse mouse
9	ɔː horse	boring awful word
10	ɪə ear	beard earrings wear
11	eə chair	hair scared fear
12	k key	crowded city across
13	tʃ chess	church beach chemist's
14	dʒ jazz	large forget giraffe

b 🔊 12.5 Listen and check.

4 READING

a Read the article and match the questions with the answers.

Don't ask me!
A survey of 2,000 parents has discovered that two thirds of them are unable to answer their children's questions about science. See if you can match the ten most common questions with their answers below.

1 Why is the moon sometimes out in the day?   *E*
2 Why is the sky blue?   —
3 Will we ever discover aliens?   —
4 How much does the Earth weigh?   —
5 How do aeroplanes stay in the air?   —
6 Why is water wet?   —
7 How do I do long multiplication?   —
8 Where do birds and bees go in winter?   —
9 What makes a rainbow?   —
10 Why are there different times on Earth?   —

A Bees stop flying and birds stay together in groups or migrate.
B People decided to have 'time zones' so that it would be light during the day everywhere on Earth. If there weren't time zones, some people would have midday in the middle of the night!
C The Earth weighs 6,000,000,000,000,000,000,000,000,000kg.
D Because of their chemistry, some liquids can be absorbed by solid things.
E The moon can be lit up by the sun, depending on where it is in the sky. If it reflects the sun's rays, we can see it, even during the day. It all depends on its angle towards the Earth.
F Multiply the single numbers and the tens separately, then add them together.
G Sunlight arrives on Earth in every colour, but it hits particles in our air that 'shine' blue.
H Planes have special wings which push air down. This pushing action is stronger than gravity, and so the plane goes up in the air.
I Sunlight going through water drops in the air 'separates' into all the colours.
J No one knows.

b Underline five words that you don't know. Use your dictionary to look up their meaning and pronunciation.

5 LISTENING

a 🔊 12.6 Listen to five people talking about quiz shows. Complete the names of the shows.

1 *Master* _____
2 *A Question of* _____
3 _____ *my Bluff*
4 *Who wants to be a* _____?
5 _____ *Quiz*

b Listen again. Match some questions which could have been on these quiz shows with the speakers.

Speaker 1   *E*   A Who sang *Every breath you take*?
Speaker 2   __   B Who painted *Sunflowers*?
                            A Picasso B Van Gogh C Cezanne D Monet
Speaker 3   __   C How many times has Brazil won the World Cup?
Speaker 4   __   D What does 'willy nilly' mean?
Speaker 5   __   E When was Charles Dickens born?

Listening

🔊 1.4

Ben Great party.
Sandra Yes, it is.
Ben Sorry…hi…my name's Ben.
Sandra I'm Sandra.
Ben What do you do, Sandra?
Sandra I'm a nurse. How about you?
Ben Me? Oh, I'm a student.
Sandra A student? Really? What university do you go to?
Ben Manchester. I go to Manchester University. I'm in my second year of medicine.
Sandra Do you like it?
Ben Yes, I do. I like it very much…

Ben What do you think of the music, Sandra? Do you like it?
Sandra No, not really.
Ben What kind of music do you listen to?
Sandra I like rock music.
Ben Do you? Who's your favourite band?
Sandra Muse. I really like Muse.
Ben Me, too. Did you go to the concert last month?
Sandra No, I didn't. Was it good?
Ben Yes, it was excellent. I'm sorry you missed it.

Ben Do you do any sport or exercise, Sandra?
Sandra Yes, I play tennis.
Ben Ah, nice. I play rugby. I'm in the university team.
Sandra Are you?
Ben Yes, I am. But I play tennis, too. Perhaps we can play together one day.
Sandra Maybe. But I usually play with my boyfriend.
Ben Your boyfriend?
Sandra Yes, here he is. Wayne, this is Ben. Ben, Wayne.
Wayne Hello. Nice to meet you.
Ben Hi. Um, look at the time. Um, must go – some friends are waiting for me. Um, bye Sandra.
Sandra Bye.

🔊 1.7

Presenter Hello and welcome to *Love Online*. Today, we'd like you, the listeners, to call in and tell us about your experiences of online relationships. And – oh my! – that's quick! – we already have our first caller. Hello?
Alan Hi, my name's Alan.
Presenter Hello, Alan. Can you tell us about your experience of internet dating?
Alan Yes, of course. I'm quite shy, you see, and I'm not very good at talking to girls I don't know. So one day, I registered on an online dating agency and I met Susan.
Presenter And what happened?
Alan We got on really well. In fact, after four months, we bought a house together. And now we've got a beautiful little boy called Sam.
Presenter Congratulations, Alan! Thanks for calling. Now, I think we have another caller. Hello?
Kate Hi, I'm Kate.
Presenter Hello, Kate. What can you tell us about love online?
Kate Well, I decided to try a dating site because I work long hours and I don't have time to meet new people.
Presenter So what happened?
Kate Well, I met some guys, and then I met Craig.
Presenter Who's Craig?
Kate Well, now, he's my husband. And we're very happy together.
Presenter That's great news, Kate! It looks as if it is possible to find love online. Now, who's our next caller.
Paolo Paolo.

Presenter Hi, Paolo. Did you marry someone you met on the internet?
Paolo Yes, I did, but it was the worst thing I ever did.
Presenter Oh. Why's that?
Paolo Because she didn't really love me.
Presenter How do you know that?
Paolo It was in the newspaper. There was an article about a woman who contacted men online, married them, and then left with all their money. And there was a photo of my wife next to the article, with her ex-husband.
Presenter Oh, I'm sorry to hear that, Paolo. And I'm afraid that's all we've got time for today. Join me next week for another edition of *Love Online*…

🔊 1.9

And now for the latest news in the art world. If you're in Paris this weekend, you might like to visit the new David Hockney exhibition called *Fresh Flowers*. As the name suggests, most of the pictures depict flowers. However, these are no ordinary flower pictures, because Hockney uses his iPhone or his iPad to draw them.

Hockney started painting on his iPhone during the winter of 2008. At the time, he was staying at his home in the North of England where he has a beautiful view out of his bedroom window. One morning, he picked up his iPhone, and used his fingers to paint the sunrise. He was very pleased with the result, and started experimenting with other pictures. Now, he sends his friends a different flower picture every morning. They love it!

Fresh Flowers is on at the Fondation Pierre Bergé, Yves Saint Laurent in Paris until January 30th. The exhibition shows the drawings Hockney made on an iPhone, and the pictures he drew on an iPad. The gallery is open from 11 a.m. to 6 p.m. from Tuesday to Friday, and admission costs €5. Don't miss this show; it will be a bright moment in your day.

🔊 2.3

Speaker 1 When I was 17, I went on holiday with my parents to Brittany, in France. My parents rented a lovely house on the beach, and the weather was great. We went for a delicious meal for my birthday, but I was miserable. I wanted to be with my friends and I didn't smile once in two weeks!

Speaker 2 A few years ago, I went to visit an old school friend, but I didn't enjoy the weekend at all. At school we got on really well, but now she has two small children so she didn't want to go out. I spent a very boring two days in her house watching TV. I don't think I'm going to visit her again.

Speaker 3 It's really hot where we live, so we always try to go on vacation where it's cool. Last year, we booked a vacation in Sweden, but we arrived in the middle of a heat wave. It was awful because there was no air-conditioning anywhere. We just sat in cafés and argued all day. We can do that at home!

Speaker 4 When I finished university, I went on a cruise around the Mediterranean with some friends from my course. We wanted to celebrate the end of our exams. As soon as we left the port, I started feeling seasick. I spent the whole week in bed, and I hated every minute of the cruise.

Speaker 5 Three years ago, I broke up with my boyfriend, so I decided to go on an expensive vacation on my own to the Seychelles. Unfortunately, the travel agent didn't tell me that the islands were popular with couples on their honeymoon. Everywhere I looked, there were people holding hands and I felt very lonely.

🔊 2.5

Jenny What shall we do this afternoon, Matt?
Matt I know! Let's have a look at that box of photos my aunt gave me yesterday…Here it is…Oh, look at that!
Jenny Who's that?
Matt That's my grandfather. And that's my grandmother behind him on the right. She's the one in the flowery dress. It was just after they got married, but before they had any children. My aunt told me all about this photo a few years ago.
Jenny So, where are they?
Matt Well, as you know my dad is Spanish. My grandparents lived in the centre of Madrid, and this photo was taken in the district where they lived.
Jenny What's going on exactly?
Matt Well, there's a festival there called 'La Paloma'. It takes place in the middle of August every year, and it still happens now. There are lots of stalls selling food and also stalls where you can win a prize.
Jenny So, what was your grandfather trying to win?
Matt He was trying to win a bracelet for my grandmother. He was shooting at a target on the stall and all those people were watching him.
Jenny Do you know any of the other people in the photo?
Matt No, I don't. But I think they all lived near my grandfather.
Jenny Who took the photo?
Matt The man on the stall. The photo was included in the price. You had three chances to hit the target and you got the photo for free.
Jenny It's a lovely photo. I think your granddad was very good-looking!
Matt That's what everyone says!

🔊 2.7

Presenter Hello, and welcome to the programme. Today, we're looking at lucky escapes, and Nick Williams from the news desk is here to tell us some amazing stories. Nick?
Nick Hi Gloria. Well, my first story is about a tourist who fell into a volcano. Maureen Evason was walking at the top of the Teide volcano in Tenerife, when she tripped and fell. She fell 27 metres until she hit a tree, which stopped her fall and saved her life. The rescue operation took nearly four hours, and after that Maureen spent two months in hospital before she could go home.
Presenter Lucky Maureen! What else have you got for us?
Nick Joseph Rabadue had a lucky escape when he was at home watching TV. Joseph was sitting on the floor, so his dad told him to go and sit on the sofa. Five minutes later, a lorry crashed into their living room, and threw the family television into the air. The TV then landed on the exact spot where Joseph had been on the floor before.
Presenter What a lucky escape! Do you have any more?
Nick Yes, just one more for now. One Saturday morning, Barry McRoy was leaving a café when two men came in. The men were fighting, and one of them had a gun. The man fired, and the bullet hit Barry in the chest. Luckily, he had a DVD in the pocket of his jacket at the time, and the DVD stopped the bullet. Barry McRoy is a very lucky man.
Presenter Absolutely! So, now it's time for you, the listeners, to call in and tell us about your own experiences. And here's our first caller.

🔊 **3.2**

Dialogue 1
Woman John!
Man Hi, Jane. You look well.
Woman You, too. How was your flight?
Man We took off a bit late, but it was fine.
Woman 1 Are you hungry?
Man 1 No, I had a sandwich on the plane.
Woman 1 Well, let's go and find the car. It isn't far.
Man 1 Great!

Dialogue 2
Ground staff Hello. Where are you flying to?
Passenger To Bristol.
Ground staff Can I see your passport, please?
Passenger Here you are.
Ground staff Thanks. Can I see your hand luggage?
Passenger Yes, just this bag.
Ground staff OK. Here's your boarding pass. The flight is boarding at 16.50 from Gate B28. You're in Group B.
Passenger Thanks a lot.
Ground staff Enjoy your flight.

Dialogue 3
Immigration Officer Can I see your passport please, sir?
Passenger Here you are.
Immigration Officer What is the purpose of your visit, Mr Green?
Passenger I'm going to stay with a friend.
Immigration Officer And how long are you going to stay in San Francisco?
Passenger For three weeks.
Immigration Officer Can I have a contact telephone number, please?
Passenger Yes. My friend's number is 415 673 702.
Immigration Officer Thank you, Mr Green. Enjoy your stay.

Dialogue 4
Woman 2 Look! There's a grey case. Is it ours?
Man 2 No, it's too big. Ours is much smaller.
Woman 2 It's taking a long time to come out…
Man 2 Yes. The first one came out really quickly.
Woman 2 Look! There it is! At last!
Man 2 You stay here with the other bags. I'm going to get it.
Woman 2 OK. I'll wait for you here.

Dialogue 5
Customs Officer Excuse me, madam. Can you come this way, please?
Passenger Yes, of course.
Customs Officer Have you got anything to declare?
Passenger No, I don't think so. I bought some chocolate in the Duty Free Shop, but that's all.
Customs Officer Can I check your bag, please?
Passenger Sure. Go ahead.
Customs Officer OK…That's fine. You can go on through.
Passenger Thank you.

🔊 **3.4**

Chris Hi, Dawn. I hear you're going to be on holiday next week.
Dawn Yes, I am. And I'm really looking forward to it.
Chris What are you going to do?
Dawn I'm going Interrailing with a friend.
Chris Interrailing? I did that when I was a student. I travelled around Europe with very little money, not much food, and no sleep. It was fun, but I don't want to do it again.
Dawn Ah, but you see Interrailing as an adult is very different.
Chris Really? In what way?
Dawn Well, you can travel first class now, and you don't have to go for a whole month.
Chris How long are you going for?
Dawn I wanted to go for two weeks, but work's so busy at the moment… so just a week.
Chris And which countries are you visiting?

Dawn Italy and France. We're starting in Venice, then we're going to Verona, and then Milan. We're stopping off in Paris on the way back, because I want to visit the Louvre.
Chris What about sleeping arrangements? Are you sleeping on the train like all the students do?
Dawn No, only on the night train from Paris to Venice. We have a two-bed sleeping compartment. And we're having dinner in the dining car of the train. Apart from that, we're sleeping in hotels. They're already booked.
Chris Well, it sounds like a different kind of trip to the one we went on as students.
Dawn Absolutely. It's going to be different, but I'm sure we're going to have lots of fun.

🔊 **3.6**

Presenter Hello and welcome to *The World of Words*. Today, we're going to look at word games, so let's start with the most popular of them all: *Scrabble*. Ricky Jones from the National Scrabble Association is here to tell us all about it. Ricky, who actually invented the game?
Ricky Well, it was an American called Alfred Mosher Butts. Butts was an unemployed architect, and in his free time he did a lot of crosswords. These crosswords gave him the idea for a game which he called *Lexico*. The game had the same letter tiles as *Scrabble*, but no board. Players used the letter tiles to make words. They scored by adding up the points on each of the letter tiles. Later, Butts introduced a board, and a set of rules and changed the name to *Criss-Cross Words*.
Presenter How did Butts decide how many points to give each letter?
Ricky He counted how many times each letter appeared on the front page of the *New York Times*. Then, depending on the frequency of each letter, he gave it between one and ten points. The most common letters, like the vowels, got only one point because they are easier to use. There are more of these letters in the game. There was only one tile for each of the least common letters, for example Q and Z, which got ten points.
Presenter So, when did Butts' original game become the modern game of *Scrabble*?
Ricky Well, in 1948, Butts met a businessman called James Brunot, who designed a new board and changed the name of the game to *Scrabble*. Then in 1952, the president of Macy's, the famous New York department store, discovered the game on holiday, and loved it so much he placed a large order. Butts and Brunot knew they couldn't produce enough *Scrabble* sets for Macy's, and so they sold the rights to the game to another manufacturer. Today, Scrabble is sold in 121 countries in 29 different languages.
Presenter What a story, Ricky! Thank you for sharing it with us.
Ricky My pleasure.

🔊 **4.2**

Speaker 1 Housework? Me? No, that's my mum's job. She only goes to work two days a week, so she has enough time to cook and clean and things like that. I go to school and then I see my friends, so I'm too busy to do housework. My dad goes out to work every day, so he doesn't have time either.
Speaker 2 Well, I try and help my mum when I can. I make my bed when I get up in the morning and I always lay the table for dinner. I usually tidy my room, but my mum is the one that cleans it. Apart from that, I'm not at home very much, so I don't do anything else.
Speaker 3 Oh yes, everyone in my family helps with the housework. There are four of us and we're all very busy. During the week, my mum or my dad cook the dinner, and my brother and I do the washing up. We do the cleaning together on Saturday mornings.
Speaker 4 It's true – I don't do much housework, but I love cooking. I don't have time to cook during the week, but I do all the cooking at the weekends. My mum does all the cleaning, though. She says she doesn't mind it.

Speaker 5 We have a cleaning lady who comes in every day and she does all our housework. She makes the beds, cleans the floors, and tidies our rooms – she even does the ironing! I'm not sure who does the shopping, but the fridge is always full. That's the important thing!

🔊 **4.4**

Presenter Those listeners who enjoy going shopping will be interested to hear our next news story. It's taken six years and 1.45 billion pounds to build, but at last the Westfield shopping centre has opened in Stratford, in East London. We sent our reporter, Juliet Redditch, over to take a look at what is now Europe's largest urban shopping centre. Juliet, what's it like in Westfield right now?
Juliet Well, Terry, there are crowds of people everywhere, especially outside the stores which have special opening offers. Some shops have called security staff to help them control the queues.
Presenter Just how big is Westfield, Juliet?
Juliet Oh, it's really very big! There are two enormous department stores, a huge supermarket, and 300 smaller shops. You can spend all day here if you want to. I haven't decided where I'm going to have lunch, but there are 70 different places to eat – it's amazing!
Presenter What effect has the shopping centre had on the local area, Juliet?
Juliet Well, this is an area where there are many people out of work. The shopping centre has created 10,000 new jobs, so it has really helped.
Presenter How did you get to Westfield today?
Juliet I came by car. There's an enormous car park with space for 5,000 cars. But you can also get here by bus, train, and by the underground – it's the best connected shopping centre in the country.
Presenter Now, Juliet, the big question is…have you bought anything yet?
Juliet No, I haven't. I was just looking around, really. I saw some trousers I liked, but I didn't buy them. There were too many people in the changing rooms to try them on!
Presenter OK, thanks Juliet, and now onto a news story of a different kind…

🔊 **4.6**

Speaker 1 Last weekend was really awful. My boyfriend and I went camping in the Lake District with some friends, and it rained the whole time. It was really depressing. We had to stay in the tent and play cards all day, which was OK to begin with, but then my boyfriend got bored. He started complaining about the weather, then about our friends, and finally about me! We had a terrible argument, and in the end we came home on Saturday night. I'm never going camping again!
Speaker 2 My weekend was fantastic. I took my wife to Paris, which is somewhere she has wanted to visit her whole life. We stayed in a wonderful hotel, in a beautiful old building overlooking the river. The view was incredible. We ate some really great food, and although it was quite cold, we had a very nice walk around the city. The best bit was that it was a surprise for my wife: I met her after work on Friday and we drove straight to the airport. She had no idea where we were going!
Speaker 3 I haven't got much money at the moment, so I didn't do anything special this weekend. But actually I had a really good time! I visited a local museum with some friends. All the museums here are free, and they have some interesting exhibitions about places like Egypt, Rome, and India. We then watched two of my favourite DVDs on Saturday night, and on Sunday I invited my parents to my flat and I cooked dinner for them. Not a bad weekend, really.
Speaker 4 My brother and his wife stayed with us this weekend. They have three children, and we spent the whole time playing with them. We took them swimming, we went to the zoo, and on Sunday we

went to the park. They have so much energy! And they're really noisy – especially in the morning when they wake up, which is usually around 6 o'clock. I was completely exhausted by Sunday night, but it was lovely to see them.

◎ 5.2

Speaker 1 Well, I haven't been here long, so I haven't had time to make many friends yet. After I get home from work, I spend most of the evening online chatting with friends and family back home. Twice a week, I have classes to try and learn the language. Most of my colleagues speak really good English, but I haven't been out with them yet.

Speaker 2 I guess you could say I'm a bit depressed at the moment. Time goes really slowly when you've got nothing to do. I spend more time sleeping now, and I have a lot of time to do the housework. It doesn't take all day to make the bed and clean my room, so I get quite bored. I hope I find another job soon because I really need the money.

Speaker 3 My life has changed a lot now that I don't have to leave the house to go to work. Things aren't so stressful first thing in the morning now. I just get up, make a cup of tea, and switch on my computer. It's strange communicating with colleagues online and not seeing them face-to-face. Sometimes it gets a bit lonely.

Speaker 4 Oh no, I never get bored. There's always so much to do! I like to get up early and read the newspaper while I'm having breakfast. Then I like to go for a walk and do a bit of shopping. After lunch, I go and pick up my grandchildren from school. We spend an hour in the park until their mum comes to get them. I'm really enjoying life right now.

Speaker 5 This is the best thing that has ever happened to me! She's so beautiful that I seem to spend all day looking at her! I don't have time to see friends now, so I keep in touch with everybody by phone or online when she's asleep. We go shopping together and I do more housework and cooking, but I don't get much sleep anymore!

◎ 5.4

Presenter Hello and welcome to *The Travel Programme*. Now, one of the most popular tourist destinations these days is the Republic of Croatia in the Balkans. Paula Wilcox from the National Tourist Board is here to tell us all about it. Paula, what's so special about Croatia?

Paula Oh, there's just so much to see and do there. First of all, there are historic cities like Zagreb – the capital – and Dubrovnik to visit.

Presenter Let's start with Zagreb. What is there to see there?

Paula Well, Zagreb is in the north of the country on the River Sava. It's both an old city and a modern one at the same time. There are lots of elegant restaurants and fashionable shops there, and the city has lots of museums – the most important one is the Archaeological Museum.

Presenter What about Dubrovnik?

Paula Dubrovnik is much smaller than Zagreb – the population is only about 43,000. It's in the south of Croatia on the Adriatic coast. Inside the old city walls there are palaces, churches, and a Baroque cathedral to visit. In my opinion, Dubrovnik is one of the most beautiful cities in the world.

Presenter Apart from the cities, what else would you recommend?

Paula The beaches and the islands. There are wonderful beaches on the Adriatic Sea – Croatia's coast is very long – and it has more than a thousand islands.

Presenter How can you get to the islands?

Paula Well, the best place to get a ferry is Split, another city on the coast which is larger than Dubrovnik, but also has some wonderful monuments. There are a number of ferries, which take you to many different islands, where you can do water sports or just relax on the beach.

Presenter So, when is the best time to visit Croatia, Paula?

Paula The main tourist areas are very crowded in July and August, so it's better to go in May or June, when it isn't as busy.

Presenter Thank you for that, Paula. Croatia certainly sounds like a very interesting holiday destination. Now, let's look at a different type of holiday …

◎ 5.6

Dave Hey Alice. Let's do this quiz. It says you can find out your body age.

Alice Body age? OK.

Dave You first. So…we start with your real age, which is 35…

Alice Don't tell everyone.

Dave Sorry…then we add or subtract years depending on your answers to the questions. Got that?

Alice Yes.

Dave Right. First question. How much do you walk a day?

Alice Well, I always go for a walk at lunch time. So … quite a lot.

Dave Quite a lot. OK, so we subtract one year, which leaves us with 34. Next question. How much sport and exercise do you do?

Alice Oh I hate sport. And I don't do any exercise. I guess that means none.

Dave No sport or exercise. Add two years. That makes 36. How much fast food do you eat?

Alice None. I don't eat any.

Dave Great! Subtract a year. We're back on 35 again. How many portions of fruit and vegetables do you eat?

Alice A lot. I have more than five every day.

Dave A lot. Subtract two years. That's 33. Next one. How would you describe yourself mentally?

Alice Um, what do you mean?

Dave Well, are you a positive person, or a negative person?

Alice Oh, right. Um, I think I'm a very positive person.

Dave OK. Subtract three years…Now you're on 30. Next question. How would you describe your stress level?

Alice Mmm, I would say I'm a little stressed…but it's under control.

Dave OK, so we don't have to add or subtract anything. You're still on 30. How many close friends do you see regularly?

Alice Mmm. A few. I don't have much time.

Dave Right…we don't add or subtract anything again. Last question. How much time do you have for yourself?

Alice Not enough. I'm always really busy.

Dave Add a year…That makes 31. Which means that you are 35 but your body is only 31. What do you think of that?

Alice 31? That's great news! Now it's your turn…

◎ 6.2

Matt What are you reading?

Amy Nothing. Just my horoscope.

Matt Really? What star sign are you?

Amy Virgo. My birthday's on September 15th.

Matt So, what does it say?

Amy It says that people will talk about me next week because of something I've done.

Matt But you don't really believe that, do you?

Amy Well, actually I do. Because I have done something that will make people talk about me.

Matt Oh. What have you done?

Amy I sent an email to my boss yesterday complaining about my new colleague. She's really lazy and she never does any work.

Matt Did you?

Amy Yes. So my boss will ask the other people in my office about this new person and he'll probably ask about me, too. So, my horoscope is right. People will definitely talk about me next week.

Matt Well, don't worry about it. I'm sure everything will be alright.

Amy I hope so.

Matt Anyway, what about me? What does my horoscope say?

Amy Let me have a look. Your birthday's January 5th, so that makes you…Capricorn.

Matt That's right….So, what does it say?

Amy It says…oh! Listen to this! It says you'll be lucky with money next week.

Matt Really? Perhaps I should go out and buy a lottery ticket!

Amy No, wait a minute. Let's think about this. You've got a meeting with <u>your</u> boss tomorrow, haven't you?

Matt Yes. Why?

Amy Perhaps she'll give you a pay rise!

Matt Oh, Amy! Really! You're taking this far too seriously! I don't believe a word of it!

Amy Well, I do. I think your boss will put up your salary tomorrow. Perhaps she'll offer you a better job!

Matt Amy, you're being far too optimistic. It's only a horoscope, for goodness' sake!

◎ 6.4

Speaker 1 I was on holiday, and I was looking round a famous palace, when a man came up to me and asked me to take a photo of him. He gave me his camera, but it wasn't working properly. When I gave it back to him, he dropped it on the floor and it broke. I picked it up and went to give it to the man, but he was gone. Then I discovered my wallet was missing.

Speaker 2 When I went abroad last year for a business trip, I didn't have time to get any local money before I left. So after I landed, I went straight to the bank to get three hundred euros. I was in a hurry because I had a train to catch. The cashier slowly counted out the notes and when he stopped, I picked them up. When I got to the train station I realized later that I only had a hundred euros.

Speaker 3 When we were on holiday, two men knocked on the door of our apartment. They were wearing uniforms and they said they were police inspectors. One of them came in to look around while the other stayed by the door. Unfortunately, while we were talking to the first man, the second man took our wallets and cameras from the bedroom.

Speaker 4 I was having a problem using the ticket machine in the metro, when someone came up to help me. He told me how much money I needed and then offered to put it in the machine for me. I counted out the money, but he said it wasn't enough. I gave him some more money and I got my ticket. Unfortunately, I paid ten times the price for it!

Speaker 5 I was waiting at a bus stop, when this beautiful woman came up to me. We got chatting, and she invited me to go to a club with her. We had a few drinks together and then the waiter brought me an incredibly expensive bill. I started to complain but then I noticed four big men at the door who were looking at me. Of course I paid the bill.

◎ 6.6

Presenter Hello and welcome to the programme. Do you ever have the same dream night after night? These dreams are called 'recurring dreams', and psychologist Dr William Harris is in the studio today to tell us all about them. Good morning, Dr Harris.

Dr Harris Hello.

Presenter Dr Harris, which is the most common recurring dream?

Dr Harris Well, top of the list is the dream where someone or something is running after you. Either it's a person or a dangerous animal, like a bull or a lion. The dream means that there is something in your life that you don't want to face. It can be a feeling, a conflict or a memory, for example, but whatever it is, it's something that you don't want to deal with.

Presenter Right. What's the next dream on the list?

Dr Harris It's the one where you are falling for what seems like a very long time. Falling is a definite sign that you are out of control. You have lost direction in your life and you don't know what to do.

Presenter Yes, I've had that dream before. Not recently, though. Anyway, what other recurring dreams are there?

Dr Harris This is another fairly common dream. You're trying to get somewhere but you get lost on the way, and you don't know where you are. People often have this dream when they're going through a period of change. It shows that they don't want to accept the new situation.

Presenter OK, Dr Harris. Have you got any more recurring dreams for us?

Dr Harris Yes, there are two. The first dream is a good one. Some people have a recurring dream that they are flying through the air. They are enjoying it, and enjoying looking down on the world below. This shows that they are feeling free, possibly because they have solved a problem they had, or they have escaped from a difficult situation in their life.

Presenter And the last dream?

Dr Harris This one isn't so good. It's a feeling of being trapped. Maybe you are in a lift that is trapped between floors and you can't get out. This dream means that there is something in your life that is making you feel unhappy, and you feel that you cannot change it.

Presenter Dr Harris, that was very interesting. Thank you for talking to us.

Dr Harris You're welcome.

🔊 **7.2**

Dave Oh, that's ridiculous!

Jane What is?

Dave They've decided to ban jokes about mothers-in-law!

Jane Who has?

Dave The council, of all people. They've written a leaflet for workers who have to deal with the public, and it says that mother-in-law jokes are 'offensive'.

Jane Well, I suppose they are, really. I mean, there are a lot of mothers-in-law out there, and the jokes are about them.

Dave No, but it's just a bit of fun, isn't it? I mean, I think it's really important to have a sense of humour. It's good for you – it makes you feel better.

Jane That's easy for you to say, isn't it? You're a man, so you'll never be a mother-in-law. I will, one day.

Dave Yes, but you won't be my mother-in-law, will you? Sorry, I was only joking!

Jane Ha ha…Does it say anything else about the jokes?

Dave Yes. It says they show 'disrespect for parents'.

Jane OK. Well, maybe they do. Young people are healthy, fit, and attractive. It's easy for them to laugh at older people, don't you think?

Dave Oh, come on! These jokes about mothers-in-law have been around since Roman times.

Jane Where did you get that idea from?

Dave It says here that there's a Roman writer called – hang on a minute – called 'Juvenal' who said in the first century A.D. – wait, listen to this – 'it's impossible to be happy when one's mother-in-law is still alive'. Ha ha! That's classic!

Jane Um.

Dave And all the best comedians tell jokes about mothers-in-law, too. I think they're funny.

Jane Like I said, that's because you're a man. And the comedians you're talking about are also men. It's just another example of the sexist world we live in. I mean, there aren't many jokes about fathers-in-law, are there?

Dave Oh, for goodness' sake!

🔊 **7.4**

Speaker I like singing while I'm having a shower. The bathroom is a great place to sing because nobody can hear you – at least, I hope nobody can hear, because I sing really loudly! I usually sing very old classic songs, which I'd never sing in public!

Speaker 2 I always feel like singing when I'm alone in my car on a summer's day. I turn up the radio, open the window, and sing along to whatever comes on. I don't do this in the middle of town, of course; only if I'm driving through the country, but I must say I find it really relaxing.

Speaker 3 I've always really enjoyed singing with the kids I teach – I'm a primary school teacher. Young children love singing, and they like it even more if the songs have actions. It's amazing how much they learn from songs – there are alphabet songs, counting songs, and all sorts. We always have lots of fun when we're singing together.

Speaker 4 Actually, I can't sing very well at all, so I'm always really embarrassed if I have to sing in public. When I was at secondary school, I had to be in the school choir, but I never actually sang. I just mouthed the words and pretended to sing.

Speaker 5 When I'm out with my friends, we sometimes go to a karaoke in the centre of town. It's one of my favourite places, as we always have a good time. We spend most of the evening singing together and nobody seems to mind if we do it badly. In fact, it's better if we do sing badly as it makes everybody laugh.

🔊 **7.6**

Presenter …And here's some good news for one of the world's endangered languages. There are nearly six thousand languages in the world today, and experts say that nearly half of them are dying out. That means that around three thousand languages will disappear in the next century or so. One language in danger of dying out is the Cherokee language, spoken by the Cherokee people of North America. Or at least it <u>was</u> in danger until the leaders of the tribe decided to do something about it. They got worried when they realized that only 8,000 of the 290,000 Cherokee people in the world today actually spoke the language and they came up with a plan. They got in touch with the electronics company, Apple, and asked them to include Cherokee on the official list of languages used on their products.

At first, it seemed impossible that Apple would take any notice of the Cherokee, as their products already had fifty languages on them. The big surprise came in September 2006, when the Apple iOS 4.1 operating system was released with Cherokee on the official list of languages. Since then, the Cherokee people have been able to use their language on all Mac computers, iPhones, the iPod touch, and the iPad. These devices were popular with the younger members of the tribe from the start, but now the older members are taking an interest, too – especially those who use mobile phones.

So, it looks as if the Cherokee language won't die out just yet after all. And if the language stays alive, the culture will stay alive, too, something that the leaders of the tribe will be very happy about.

🔊 **8.2**

Speaker 1 I don't usually talk about my problems, but if something's going wrong, I sometimes mention it to Phil. He's on my basketball team, and we get along OK. In fact, he's the one who introduced me to the girl I'm dating at the moment.

Speaker 2 The person who I talk to most is my sister. We don't look like each other at all, but we both have very similar personalities. She's a really good listener, and she always gives me good advice. She sometimes tells me her problems too, and I try to help her.

Speaker 3 My friend Jenny is on my course at university, and I tell her absolutely everything. We're quite different, which means we often think in different ways. Sometimes we argue, but we're never angry with each other for long – just until one of us apologizes.

Speaker 4 The person who understands me most is my friend John, who lives next door. We've grown up together, so he knows me very well. My main problem at the moment is my job, which I hate. John thinks I should look for a new one, and he's probably right.

Speaker 5 My gran lives with us, and I spend a lot of time talking to her. Although she's older than me, she's

always interested in what I have to say. We've got quite a lot in common, and some things that have happened to me also happened to her when she was young.

🔊 **8.4**

Presenter Now, everyone loves travelling, and we all enjoy telling stories about the places we've been to. But what happens if there's an earthquake while you're away? Travel expert, Monica Fields, is here in the studio with us today to give us some tips on what to do in a natural disaster. First of all, Monica, is it possible to avoid them?

Monica Well, no, actually, it isn't. Nobody really knows exactly when a disaster like a forest fire or a blizzard will happen, so you can't really avoid them. What you can do, however, is be prepared.

Presenter How can you do that?

Monica Well, first of all, if you plan to visit a region where there are natural disasters at certain times of the year, try not to go at that time. For example, there are often bad storms, hurricanes, or cyclones in the Caribbean in May and June, so don't go there then.

Presenter That sounds sensible. What else can you do?

Monica It's really important to buy travel insurance before you go. This will pay for extra nights in a hotel, for example, if you can't fly home and have to stay in your resort longer than you had planned. I never understand why some people don't take out travel insurance.

Presenter Right. So, what should you do if a natural disaster actually happens while you're abroad?

Monica The first thing you should do is to stay calm and be patient.

Presenter That sounds easy, Monica, but natural disasters can be very frightening, can't they?

Monica Yes, of course, but if you panic, things will only get worse. Secondly, you need to contact your family and friends at home as soon as possible. If they hear about the disaster on the news, they'll be incredibly worried.

Presenter Yes, I can see that. What else should you do?

Monica Well, it's always a good idea to know what your airline will do if there's a natural disaster. If you are flying to a country where natural disasters are frequent, you should ask your airline when you book your ticket if they will change your ticket if you need to leave the country quickly, or if you have to stay longer because there is a natural disaster.

Presenter Thank you for joining us, Monica, and thanks for your useful advice.

🔊 **8.6**

Ewan Did you watch TV last night, Helen?

Helen No, I didn't. What was on?

Ewan There was a really interesting cooking programme on after dinner.

Helen Was there? What made it so good?

Ewan Well, it was a sort of experiment, really. They were trying to answer the question: do men and women cook differently?

Helen Really? So what did they do to try to find the answer?

Ewan They invited a male cook and a female cook to prepare five different courses of a meal. Both cooks had to use the same main ingredient for each course, but they didn't have to make the same dish. Then, they served the dishes to a panel of judges, who tasted them, and decided if they were made by the man or the woman.

Helen Who were the judges?

Ewan Well, there were two men and two women. They were all food experts – either chefs themselves or restaurant critics.

Helen What about the cooks? Were they professionals, too?

Ewan Yes. They were from two of the best restaurants in the country.

Helen And what sort of things did they cook?

Ewan All kinds of things really, but the only ones I remember are a meat dish with garlic and a bright pink dessert.

Helen What was so special about those two dishes?

Ewan I remember them because the judges had real problems in deciding if they were made by the male chef or the female chef. In the end, they all got it wrong!

Helen So, did they manage to answer the question, then? Do men cook differently from women?

Ewan Not really. The only conclusion they came to was that it was impossible to tell if a particular dish was made by a man or a woman. That's all, really.

Helen So, it was a bit of a waste of time then, really.

Ewan No, it wasn't! I really enjoyed the programme, even if they didn't answer the question!

◍ 9.2

Newsreader And our final story on tonight's programme is about an Australian diver who has survived a shark attack. 46-year-old Eric Nerhus was fishing off the coast of Cape Howe, New South Wales, when a great white shark attacked him. He was under the water at the time, and he didn't see the animal swimming towards him. Mr Nerhus's head, shoulders, and one of his arms ended up in the shark's mouth, but, fortunately, he was wearing a heavy metal vest. When the shark tried to bite the man in half, its teeth hit the vest and not his body. Mr Nerhus knew he had to do something, so he felt for the shark's eye with the hand of his other arm. When he found it, he surprised the animal by pressing his fingers into its eye. The shark reacted by opening its mouth, giving Mr Nerhus a chance to escape. Despite his injuries, Eric managed to swim up to the surface of the water. His son pulled him onto his boat, and took him quickly to the shore. Meanwhile, another friend called the emergency services. Mr Nerhus was flown to hospital by helicopter. He had deep cuts all over his body and a broken nose, but he was very lucky to be alive. Attacks by great white sharks usually result in death because of their size and strength. The shark that attacked Mr Nerhus was over three metres long.

◍ 9.4

Presenter Hello, and welcome to the programme. Today, we've got psychologist, Dr Chris Hopper, in the studio with us to answer your questions about phobias. Hello, Chris.

Chris Good morning.

Presenter And our first caller is Cynthia Sharp from Dundee. What's your question, Cynthia?

Cynthia Um, hello, Dr Hopper. Um, my question is actually about our son, James. He's six years old, and he had a bad experience with a dog last night.

Chris I'm sorry to hear that, Cynthia. What exactly happened?

Cynthia Well, we were outside a neighbour's house, and, um, I was chatting with the mum when one of their dogs ran out. It was a big dog, um, and it came running out of the house barking. James panicked, and tried to hide behind me, but the dog jumped on him and bit him. It wasn't a serious injury, but we're very worried that he'll be afraid of dogs now. We don't want him to get a phobia. What should we do?

Chris Well, Cynthia, you're quite right to be worried about this incident because, cynophobia, that is, a fear of dogs, is often caused by a bad experience with a dog as a child. The best thing you can do is to give your son a positive experience with a different dog as soon as possible. If you have any friends who have a quiet and friendly dog, go and visit them. Let your son touch the dog if he wants to and don't remind him about his bad experience.

Presenter That sounds like good advice, Chris. And our next caller is Marion Williams from Cardiff. Marion?

◍ 9.6

Presenter Hello and welcome to those of you who just joined us. Continuing on our theme of celebrity families, the focus of today's programme is actress and singer, Judy Garland, and her daughter, Liza Minnelli.

Now, Judy Garland's real name was Frances Ethel Gumm, and she was born on June 10th, 1922 in Grand Rapids, Minnesota. Her parents ran a theatre and Judy first appeared on stage singing a Christmas song with her two older sisters when she was two years old. When she was 13, Judy joined the film company Metro Goldwyn Mayer and at the age of 16, she played Dorothy in *The Wizard of Oz*. The film was extremely successful, and she won a children's Oscar for her performance. Metro Goldwyn Mayer terminated her contract in 1950 because of her problems with alcohol and drugs. However, she continued to perform, and in 1964 she did a series of concerts at the London Palladium. In fact, it was in London where Judy Garland was found dead after she took a drug overdose in 1969. Judy got married five times and had three children. One of these children was Liza Minnelli who was 23 when her mother died.

Liza was born in Hollywood, California, on March 12th, 1946. She grew up in film studios, and, like her mother, made her first stage appearance at the age of two. She was only five when her parents got divorced. After performing successfully with her mother at the London Palladium in 1964, Liza became a professional nightclub singer. She made several albums, and later starred as a singer in the 1972 film, *Cabaret*, a role for which she won an Oscar. Despite her successful singing and acting career, Liza has had similar problems to her mother. She has been to rehab clinics several times because of her addiction to drugs and alcohol. She has also been married four times, but, unlike her mother, she never had children. Today, Liza Minnelli is in her sixties, but she still makes occasional television appearances.

◍ 10.2

Presenter Hello, and welcome to the programme. Today we have scientist, Doug McLeod, in the studio with us. He's going to tell us about some of the everyday things we know and love that were invented by accident. Doug?

Doug Hello, Janet. Well, I'm going to start with the microwave oven. In 1945, an engineer called Percy Spencer was testing some new radar equipment. He had a chocolate bar in his pocket, and while he was standing in front of the machine, it melted. After that, he also tried using the microwaves from the radar equipment to cook popcorn. Percy realized that microwaves could heat and cook food, and so the microwave oven was born.

Presenter How interesting! What else have you got for us, Doug?

Doug Next is something that is found in hospitals all over the world: the X-ray machine. In 1895, a German physicist called Wilhelm Roentgen was experimenting with electrical rays in a dark room. He was directing them through a glass tube covered with black paper. Suddenly, he saw a light on a screen on the wall and he realized that the rays could pass through the glass and the paper. After that, he experimented with his own hand, and found that he could see the bones. The first X-ray ever made was an image of Roentgen's wife's hand – you can even see her wedding ring!

Presenter That's fascinating, Doug. We've got time for one more.

Doug Many different kinds of food were discovered by accident, Janet, and I've chosen something that we call 'crisps', but Americans call 'potato chips'. These were invented by a chef called George Crum, who was working in a restaurant near Saratoga Springs, New York. A customer complained that the chips he was served were too thick. The chef was angry about this, so he fried some very thin potatoes and covered them with salt. The customer loved them, and after that 'Saratoga chips' became popular all over the USA. Eventually, they were produced for people to eat at home.

Presenter Thanks for joining us.

◍ 10.4

Tony Amy, did you study foreign languages at secondary school?

Amy Yes, I did. Actually, I used to be quite good at languages.

Tony Which ones did you study?

Amy Well, I did French for five years, then I did German for six years, and I studied Spanish for a year in my lunch break.

Tony And how much French can you remember?

Amy Not much! But I can remember my German, because I did it for my degree at Cambridge. Why all the questions, Tony?

Tony Well, I've just read this article about the state of language learning in schools in the UK, and it isn't looking good. It says that adults only remember about seven words from the languages they studied at school.

Amy Only seven words? That isn't very good, is it? What sort of words do they remember?

Tony Common words, like *Hello, Goodbye, Please, Thank you, beer, one, two* and *three*, and the question *Do you speak English?*

Amy So, what happens when people are abroad? Do they practise the language?

Tony Not at all. In fact, the article suggests that people often choose not to go on holiday to countries where they have to worry about language problems.

Amy That's probably because they're too lazy to learn a language.

Tony No, it isn't that. The article says it's because they're too embarrassed to try and speak it.

Amy OK. So which languages do pupils study at school today?

Tony Hang on a minute, there's a list here somewhere… Here it is. It says 65% of pupils study French, 25% study German, 22% Spanish, and 2% Italian. Polish is becoming more popular, too.

Amy And what are schools going to do about the problem?

Tony Well, first of all, they're going to introduce language classes for children in primary schools. And then they're going to start offering languages from outside Europe, for example Mandarin Chinese and Urdu.

Amy That sounds quite difficult. Anyway, Tony, which languages did you use to study at school?

Tony Only French. And I was terrible at it!

◍ 10.6

Speaker 1 I made a bad decision once when I was travelling home to Plymouth from university in Manchester, a journey of nearly 450 km. The choice was going by train or by bus, and I opted for the train as it was quicker. Unfortunately, the train broke down on the way, so in the end I took two hours longer than I expected.

Speaker 2 The worst decision I ever made was giving my son a skateboard for his tenth birthday. On the morning of his birthday, we went down to the park to try it out. Sadly, he fell off the board as soon as he got on it, and broke his arm. We had to cancel his birthday party, and we spent the whole day in hospital instead.

Speaker 3 I had two job interviews and both companies offered me a job. In the first job, they offered me more money, but it was a long way from where I live – an hour travelling every day. The second job was less money, but it was very near my house. In the end, I chose the second job instead, and I'm very happy I did, because last month the first company closed down.

Speaker 4 On one occasion, I had to decide between a good friend of mine and a boy I really liked. I was going to a concert with my friend, and then this boy asked me to go to the cinema with him on the same night. In the end, I said no to the boy, and went to the concert with my friend. I found out later that the boy already had a girlfriend, so I think I made the right decision.

Speaker 5 You won't believe what happened to me! I used to play the lottery with some colleagues at work. One day, I decided that I was fed up with never winning, so I stopped playing. My colleagues carried on without me, and just one week later, they had the winning numbers! They won a lot of money, and I didn't get any of it!

🔊 11.2

Speaker 1 The worst loser I know is my mum. We often used to play cards together when I was little, and if my mum was losing, it was safer to stop playing. She was always happy when she was winning, but when she was losing, you could see her getting angrier and angrier until she exploded. Sometimes, she used to go out of the room, because she was so upset!

Speaker 2 I once had a friend who was a bad loser at tennis. In fact, we stopped talking to each other because of a tennis match. We were about twenty at the time, and on this occasion we were arguing over a point. I said the ball was out and she said it was in. In the end, she just threw her racket into the net and left. We've never spoken since.

Speaker 3 I have to be very careful at work when we're talking about football. I have a colleague who gets really upset when his team loses, and he hates it if you make a joke about it. I tried it once, and he just stood up, walked out, and closed the door with a bang. He didn't speak to me for days after that, so I don't think I'll try it again.

Speaker 4 My son is a very bad loser, in fact he always has been. He's 12 now, but he still hates losing. We used to play board games together when he was little, but he always used to cry if he didn't win. I had to choose between letting him win all the time, or making him upset if I won. In the end, I stopped playing that kind of game with him.

Speaker 5 One of the guys who plays basketball with me gets incredibly upset during games, and he spends most of the time shouting at the other players. He's a really nervous person at the best of times, but when we're losing, it really is too much. The referee throws him off the court at least twice a month, and once our coach told him to go home.

🔊 11.4

Interviewer Can I ask you about your job, Graham?
Graham Yes, of course. Go ahead.
Interviewer What time do you go to bed?
Graham Well, I don't often get home before six o'clock in the morning, and it usually takes me a little while to relax. It's probably about seven by the time I go to sleep.
Interviewer And what time do you have to get up again?
Graham I usually get up at one o'clock, to have lunch with my family. After that, I go back to bed again for an hour or so, until about three o'clock.
Interviewer Do you need an alarm clock to wake up?
Graham No, I never use one. I wake up the first time when my children come home from school for lunch. The second time, my wife wakes me up. That's when I get up properly.
Interviewer How do you feel when you wake up?
Graham It depends on the day, really. If I've only worked for a day or two, I'm full of energy, but if it's after the fifth or sixth night in a row, I'm absolutely exhausted. That's when I find it really hard to get out of bed.
Interviewer What do you do about meals, Graham?
Graham Well, like I said, my first meal of the day is what you would call lunch. Then, I have dinner at about midnight with some other drivers in a café. When I get home in the morning, I have something light, like a ham sandwich or some toast before I go to bed.
Interviewer Would you like to change your working hours, Graham?
Graham If I changed my working hours, I wouldn't earn as much money! There's a lot more work at night, because people go out for dinner and to the theatre or clubs, and then it's late and they need to get home, and they don't want to drive because they've usually had a drink or two. I quite enjoy my job, really, because I meet lots of interesting people.

🔊 11.7

Presenter And to finish off today's programme, we're going to take a look at some famous twins. Let's start with probably the earliest set of twins in history: Romulus and Remus. Now, the legend says that they were abandoned by their parents, because twins were thought to bring bad luck. Fortunately, they were found by a female wolf, who looked after them when they were babies. According to legend, the boys grew up, and later founded the city of Rome. After some time, they began to argue, and eventually Romulus killed Remus. As Romulus was the only brother alive, the city was called Rome after him.

Let's move on in history to the 1950s, when a set of twins called the Kray Brothers caused a lot of trouble in London's East End. Ronnie and Reggie Kray were both nightclub owners. They had expensive lifestyles, and through their nightclubs they met several American stars like Frank Sinatra and Judy Garland. However, they were also incredibly violent gangsters, and they became the leaders of organized crime in the city. They were involved in many robberies and murders, until they were eventually arrested in 1969. They were both sent to prison for life, and they both died when they were in their sixties.

On a happier note, the youngest twins ever to become famous are the Olsen twins. Mary Kate and Ashley Olsen were given the same role on the American TV series *Full House* when they were only six months old. They played the part of a little girl, and they played the same part for eight years. The producers used both sisters to play the same part, so that they didn't break the law on the number of hours a child could work. The show was very popular with American audiences. Today, the twins have grown up, and they have a fashion business.

And I'm afraid that's all we have time for. Join me, Roy Thompson, at 4 o'clock tomorrow afternoon for another two hours of *Thompson's Choice*. Bye for now.

🔊 12.2

Newsreader And now it's time for the news. Police have found the 82-year-old man who went missing last Monday evening. Dennis Leighton was found in his car on the M25 motorway. He had left home on Monday morning to drive to his daughter's house, a distance of about 90 kilometres. However, Mr Leighton had got lost, and he had spent 30 hours driving round in circles trying to find the right exit. Mr Leighton had stopped at several service stations to sleep, but he then carried on driving. After being treated in hospital for hypothermia, he has finally been reunited with his family.

A tourist had a lucky escape yesterday while she was doing a bungee jump off the Victoria Falls in Zambia. Twenty-two-year-old Erin Langworthy fell into the river because her bungee rope had broken when she jumped. She landed in the water with her feet still tied to the broken rope, and then she swam to safety. Ms Langworthy was taken straight to hospital after the accident, but had no serious injuries.

A Swedish woman has found the white gold wedding ring that she lost over 16 years ago. Lena Paahlsson had taken off the ring while she was cooking with her daughters. When she went to put it back on again, it had disappeared. That is, until yesterday, when she was picking vegetables in her garden, and she found the ring around a carrot. The ring doesn't fit Mrs Paahlsson any more, but she is going to have it made bigger.

An Australian woman had a frightening experience last night, when she discovered an adult crocodile in her living room. Forty-two-year-old Jo Dodd got out of bed when she heard her dog barking. When she opened the bedroom door, she saw a crocodile in the middle of the room. Mrs Dodd woke her husband, who called the local Crocodile Management Centre, and a crocodile catcher came to take the animal away. The crocodile had escaped from a nearby crocodile farm earlier in the week.

And that's all for now. I'll be back again at 9 o'clock for the next news bulletin.

🔊 12.4

Alan Who do you think gossips more, Jess? Men or women?
Jess Well, I gossip quite a lot with my female colleagues at work, so I suppose that women are the biggest gossips. What do you think?
Alan Yes, that's what I thought too, but it says here that it's actually men who are the biggest gossips. That's what the results of this survey say, anyway.
Jess What survey?
Alan This one here in the newspaper. It says the survey was carried out by a telecommunications company. They wanted to do research into gossiping for a new service they're offering. The aim of the survey was to find out what sort of people enjoy gossiping, and how much time they spend doing it.
Jess So what did they find out?
Alan Well, they had quite a big surprise. The study showed that a fifth of the men they interviewed said they spent at least three hours a day gossiping.
Jess Wow! That's a lot! And where do they usually gossip?
Alan Most of them said they usually gossiped at work. Hang on…I can give you the exact figures. Yes, here we go…55 per cent of the men said they gossiped at work compared to 46 per cent of the women.
Jess Goodness! I didn't realize men had so much to say! Did they tell the researchers what they usually talked about?
Alan Yes. They said that their main topics of conversation were their women colleagues, and who in the company would get the next promotion.
Jess The bit about women colleagues doesn't surprise me in the least. So, what about the women in the survey? Did they say what they talked about?
Alan Yes, they did. They told the researchers that they talked about the problems they were having in their families. They also chatted about what was happening in their favourite TV series.
Jess OK. So what about you, Alan? Do you ever gossip at work?
Alan What? Me? No, never! I wouldn't dream of it!

🔊 12.6

Speaker 1 I used to watch a quiz show called *Mastermind*. It was a very serious show, and the quizmaster was Magnus Magnusson. Each of the four contestants had to answer two rounds of questions: firstly, on their specialist subject, for example, Dickens, or the Second World War, and then on general knowledge. The thing I remember most is the quizmaster's catch phrase, 'I've started, so I'll finish.'

Speaker 2 My favourite quiz show is *A Question of Sport*. It's been on TV for years – since 1968, in fact, and, although I don't watch it any more, it's still very popular. There are two teams with the same captain each time, and all of the guests are sportsmen and women. The teams have to answer questions about sport, and the show is quite amusing, actually.

Speaker 3 I used to watch *Call my Bluff*, a quiz show about words. There were always two teams made up of a captain and two celebrities. Each team was given a word, a very unusual word, and the three team members had to give a different definition – one was true and the other two were false. The other team had to guess the correct definition. It used to be quite funny.

Speaker 4 I've always enjoyed the quiz show, *Who wants to be a Millionaire?* It started in the UK in 1998, and it's still on TV today. In each show, one contestant is asked a series of questions, and they have to choose the right answer out of four possible options. It's quite exciting, really, as the contestant can win up to a million pounds if they're good.

Speaker 5 My favourite quiz show when I was a teenager was *Pop Quiz*. It wasn't on for long – only a couple of years – but I used to love it. There were two teams made up of a captain, who was the same person each time, and some guests, who were all pop stars. The teams had to answer different questions about pop music and musicians, and I used to watch it every week.

Answer key

1A

1 GRAMMAR

a 2 Do you have any brothers or sisters?
3 What university do you go to?
4 What languages can you speak?
5 Where did you study English before?
6 What kind of music do you listen to?
7 How often do you do exercise?
8 Where did you go last weekend?

b 2 did you do last night
3 TV programmes does your girlfriend watch
4 is your birthday
5 are you from
6 did your friends go on holiday last year
7 do you read
8 were you angry yesterday

2 VOCABULARY

a 2 d 3 i 4 g 5 e 6 h 7 b 8 a 9 f 10 c

3 PRONUNCIATION

a 2 P 3 R 4 M 5 B 6 K 7 I

c 2 programme 3 thirteen 4 thirty
5 university 6 weekend 7 magazine
8 sister 9 language 10 address

4 SPELLING AND NUMBERS

a 2 seventeen, eighteen
3 eighty, ninety
4 one hundred, one hundred and one
5 eight hundred, nine hundred
6 four hundred and fifty, five hundred
7 five thousand, seven thousand
8 thirty thousand, forty thousand

b 2 exercise 3 breakfast 4 family
5 cinema 6 thousand 7 teacher
8 university 9 weekend 10 important

5 LISTENING

a Because some friends are waiting for him. / Because Sandra's boyfriend arrives.

b 1 T 2 F 3 F 4 T 5 T 6 F

1B

1 GRAMMAR

a 2 It doesn't rain a lot here
3 We don't live in a flat
4 I don't play tennis
5 He doesn't have a beard
6 They don't go to the gym
7 She doesn't write a blog

b 2 Does 3 do 4 Does 5 do 6 Does
7 Does

c 2 earns 3 study 4 want 5 lives
6 share 7 have 8 doesn't come
9 doesn't like 10 prefer 11 don't see
12 get on

2 VOCABULARY

a 2 bald 3 straight, curly
4 beard, moustache 5 fat, slim
6 thin, overweight 7 red, medium height

b 2 d 3 e 4 a 5 b 6 f

c 2 extrovert 3 mean 4 unfriendly 5 lazy
6 unkind 7 funny 8 intelligent

3 PRONUNCIATION

a 2 lives 3 likes 4 starts 5 leaves
6 cooks

c 2 extrovert 3 unfriendly 4 generous
5 moustache 6 serious 7 curly 8 quiet
9 overweight

4 READING

b 2 T 3 F 4 F 5 T

5 LISTENING

a three

c 1 E 2 A, F 3 B, D

1C

1 VOCABULARY

a Down: 2 leggings 3 trousers 4 shirt
6 tracksuit 7 cap
Across: 3 trainers 5 belt 8 coat
9 dress 10 tie

b 2 on the left 3 in front of 4 next to
5 behind 6 between

2 GRAMMAR

a 2 are relaxing 3 are walking 4 is lying
5 is relaxing 6 are sitting 7 are they doing
8 are waiting 9 are watching 10 is playing

b 2 drives 3 are sleeping 4 's raining
5 drinks 6 like 7 works 8 wears
9 're studying 10 live

3 PRONUNCIATION

a /ə/: fashion, sandals, sweater, trainers, trousers
/ɜː/: shirt, skirt, T-shirt, third, world

4 LISTENING

a David Hockney used his iPhone and iPad to draw them.

b 1 In Paris.
2 The sunrise.
3 He sends them to his friends.
4 30 January.
5 Five euros.

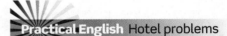

Practical English Hotel problems

1 CALLING RECEPTION

2 There's a problem with the shower.
3 I'll send somebody up right away.
4 I'm sorry to bother you again.
5 I have a problem with the Wi-Fi.
6 I'll put you through to IT.

2 SOCIAL ENGLISH

2 good view 3 looking forward
4 must be 5 By the way

3 READING

a 2 T 3 T 4 F 5 T 6 F 7 F

2A

1 VOCABULARY

a 2 for, walk 3 book 4 abroad
5 hire 6 out 7 stay 8 sightseeing
9 sunbathe 10 away

b 2 sunny 3 crowded 4 delicious
5 unhelpful 6 basic 7 friendly 8 lovely
9 cloudy 10 disgusting

2 GRAMMAR

a Regular: arrived, asked, invited, rented, stayed, sunbathed
Irregular: bought, could, chose, ate, felt, said

b 2 They didn't buy
3 The people weren't
4 I didn't sunbathe
5 We didn't hire
6 He didn't spend
7 Our room wasn't

c 2 wanted 3 booked 4 took 5 arrived
6 went 7 asked 8 looked 9 couldn't
10 went

d 2 did they want
3 did they book
4 did they arrive
5 did the woman at the desk
6 did they go

3 PRONUNCIATION

a 2 wanted 3 booked 4 invited

c 1 caught, saw 2 rang, sat 3 drove, wrote
   4 said, went 5 gave, made

4 LISTENING

a 2 c 3 d 5 e 4

1 GRAMMAR

a 2 was snowing 3 weren't driving
   4 was he doing 5 were you crying
   6 was sitting 7 were living 8 wasn't working

b 2 He fell off his bike when he was
     cycling home
   3 The children were playing video games
     when the visitors arrived
   4 We were having a barbecue when it
     started to rain
   5 I was finishing my report when my
     computer crashed

c 2 were having 3 got 4 was speaking
   5 noticed 6 was sitting 7 decided
   8 went 9 said 10 stopped 11 was passing
   12 took 13 came 14 was smiling
   15 looked 16 was laughing

2 VOCABULARY

a 2 in 3 on, in, at, on 4 on 5 on
   6 at, in, at 7 in, on 8 At, in, in

b 2 on, in 3 on, in, on 4 in, on 5 at 6 on,
   on 7 at, in 8 at, at

4 LISTENING

a Yes.

b 2 b 3 c 4 a 5 a

1 GRAMMAR

a 2 Next day 3 when 4 Suddenly
   5 Two minutes later 6 After that

b 1b so 1c Although 2a Although
   2b so 2c because 3a but 3b Although
   3c because

c 2 but I had a great holiday in Egypt
   3 although I don't really like him
   4 so I called the police
   5 although he has a lot of money
   6 because she couldn't find her wallet

2 VOCABULARY

a 2 g 3 f 4 b 5 h 6 a 7 e 8 c

3 PRONUNCIATION

a 1 awful, birthday, evening, perfect,
     restaurant, second

   2 again, although, because, invite

4 READING

a 2, 5, 1, 4, 3

5 LISTENING

2 F 3 F 4 T 5 F 6 T

1 GRAMMAR

a 2 'm going to book
   3 isn't going to sleep
   4 's, going to get
   5 isn't going to fly
   6 're going to be
   7 'm not going to stay
   8 Are, going to need

b 2 we aren't going to go
   3 We're going to go
   4 are you going to travel
   5 We're going to be
   6 are you going to do
   7 We're going to stay
   8 we're going to rent
   9 Is it going to be
   10 it isn't going to rain

2 VOCABULARY

2 lift 3 Departures 4 check-in 5 gate
6 passport control 7 Baggage Reclaim
8 trolley 9 Customs 10 Arrivals

4 READING

a three

b 2 T 3 F 4 T 5 T 6 F

5 LISTENING

a Dialogue 2 Check-in
   Dialogue 3 Immigration
   Dialogue 4 Baggage reclaim
   Dialogue 5 Customs

c 1 a sandwich 2 B28 3 415 673 702
   4 grey 5 some chocolate

1 GRAMMAR

a 2 're driving 3 aren't stopping 4 're getting
   5 're going 6 aren't taking 7 're stopping
   8 're arriving 9 're picking 10 're catching

b 2 ✓
   3 it's going to be
   4 he's going to get
   5 aren't going to miss
   6 ✓
   7 ✓
   8 she's going to have

2 VOCABULARY

2 in 3 about 4 for 5 on 6 to 7 at 8 of

3 PRONUNCIATION

a 2 I'd love to.
   3 Are you free this weekend?
   4 Sorry, no. I'm working on Saturday.
   5 What about next weekend? What are you
     doing then?
   6 Nothing. Next weekend is fine.
   7 Great. Do you like walking?
   8 I love it!
   9 OK. Let's go to Devon – the countryside
     is beautiful!

4 READING

a nine

b 2 B 3 P 4 B 5 V 6 P

5 LISTENING

a Italy and France

b 2 a student 3 a week 4 Venice
   5 the Louvre 6 in hotels

1 GRAMMAR

a 2 a 3 d 4 h 5 b 6 g 7 e 8 c

b 2 which 3 who 4 which 5 which
   6 where 7 who 8 where 9 where
   10 who

2 VOCABULARY

2 kind 3 similar 4 like 5 something
6 example 7 someone 8 somewhere

3 PRONUNCIATION

a 2 a quite, b quiet 3 a shoes, b socks
   4 a sweet, b suit 5 a sightsee, b sunbathe
   6 a weight, b height 7 a shirt, b shorts
   8 a cloudy, b crowded

4 READING

a 2 fashionista 3 Chick lit 4 E-waste
   5 sandwich generation 6 Agritourism
   7 Netiquette 8 staycation

5 LISTENING

a three

b 2 F 3 T 4 T 5 F 6 F 7 T 8 T

1 VOCABULARY

2 menu   3 starter   4 main course
5 waiter / waitress   6 dessert   7 bill

2 AT THE RESTAURANT

2 Yes, please.
3 Can I get you something to start with?
4 No, thank you. Just a main course. I'd like the steak, please.
5 And how would you like your steak? Rare, medium or well done?
6 Rare, please.
7 Would you like that with fries or with a baked potato?
8 A baked potato, please.
9 OK. And to drink?
10 Water, please.
11 Still or sparkling?
12 Still.
13 Here's your steak, madam.
14 I'm sorry but I asked for my steak rare and this is well done.

3 SOCIAL ENGLISH

1 start with   2 any suggestions, be great
3 we have   4 a mistake, my day   5 to go

4 READING

a 2 5 p.m.–7 p.m.   3 $12.95   4 214 E.9th St
5 Restaurants in the Theatre District
6 $30–$45   7 At lunchtime
7 Scandinavian food

1 VOCABULARY

a 2 make   3 tidy   4 lay   5 clean   6 take out
7 do   8 put away

b 2 make   3 make   4 do   5 do   6 make
7 do   8 make

2 GRAMMAR

a 2 Have you made any plans for the weekend yet
3 We haven't finished lunch yet
4 Daniel has already tidied his room
5 I've already done the ironing
6 Have you been to the supermarket yet
7 I haven't cleaned the bathroom yet
8 Edward has already taken out the rubbish

b 2 's just fallen   3 've just won
4 've just cleaned   5 's just laid
6 've just missed

3 PRONUNCIATION

a 2 young   3 year   4 yellow   5 uniform
6 jacket   7 teenager   8 bridge   9 jumper
10 enjoy

4 READING

a 2

b 2 F   3 T   4 T   5 F   6 F   7 T

5 LISTENING

a Speaker 3

b Speaker 2 E,   Speaker 3 A,   Speaker 4 D,
Speaker 5 C

1 VOCABULARY

a 2 changing rooms   3 checkout   4 receipt
5 suit   6 size   7 fit   8 take, back
9 shop assistants

b Down: 2 item   5 auction   7 website
Across: 3 basket   4 payment   6 checkout
8 delivery

2 GRAMMAR

a 2 I haven't brought my credit card
3 Has Anna gone / been shopping
4 Has your sister ever worked as a model
5 You haven't worn your new shirt
6 Have I ever told you about my holiday in Greece
7 The shopping centre's never been so crowded
8 I've never used eBay

b 2 **A** Have you ever sold, **B** have, **A** did you sell, **B** didn't want   3 **A** Have you ever worn, **B** haven't   4 **A** Have you ever lost, **B** have, left   5 **A** Have you ever had, **B** have, didn't have, couldn't

3 PRONUNCIATION

a 2 proceed   3 clothes   4 card

4 LISTENING

a A shopping centre

b 2 £1.45 billion
3 Two department stores, one supermarket, and 300 smaller shops
4 70
5 10,000
6 By car, bus, train, and by the underground
7 Some trousers
8 Because there were too many people in the changing rooms to try them on

1 GRAMMAR

a 2 anything   3 anywhere   4 anywhere
5 anyone   6 something   7 nobody
8 somewhere   9 somebody

b 2 T   3 T   4 F   5 T   6 F   7 F

2 VOCABULARY

2 relaxing   3 boring   4 depressed
5 interested   6 exciting   7 depressing
8 relaxed   9 bored   10 excited

3 PRONUNCIATION

a 1 anything, dress, friendly, sweater, website
2 coat, don't, goes, home, photos
3 funny, gloves, lunch, something, nothing

4 READING

a 2 Tidy your wardrobe
3 Listen to some podcasts
4 Play board games
5 Bake a loaf of bread
6 Learn how to juggle
7 Meet your neighbours
8 Organize your shelves
9 Take some photos
10 Start a blog

5 LISTENING

a Speaker 1 went camping in the Lake District.
Speaker 2 stayed in a hotel in Paris.
Speaker 3 went to a local museum.
Speaker 4's brother and wife came to stay.

b 1 Speaker 3   2 Speaker 4   3 Speaker 2
4 Speaker 3   6 Speaker 4   8 Speaker 2

1 GRAMMAR

a 2 worse   3 more slowly   4 hotter
5 harder   6 further   7 better   8 healthier
9 more dangerous   10 busier

b 2 as stylish as her shoes
3 as big as my boss's
4 play as well as Spain
5 drive as carefully as me
6 as expensive as laptops
7 look as relaxed as Harry
8 as dirty as his shirt

2 VOCABULARY

2 spend   3 on   4 waste   5 save   6 in

3 PRONUNCIATION

a 2 <u>ce</u>ntre   3 <u>pa</u>rents   4 <u>a</u>go   5 <u>chi</u>ldren
6 <u>pa</u>tient   7 <u>pro</u>blem   8 communi<u>ca</u>tion
9 tra<u>di</u>tional   10 a<u>round</u>   11 <u>se</u>conds
12 <u>be</u>tter

b 2 cen tre   3 pa r e nts   4 a go
5 chil dr e n   6 pa ti e nt   7 pro bl e m
8 c o mmuni ca ti o n   9 tra di ti o nal
10 a round   11 se co nds   12 be tt e r

4 READING

b 2 F   3 T   4 T   5 F   6 F

5 LISTENING

a 1 Speaker 3
   2 Speaker 5
   3 Speaker 2
   5 Speaker 4

b Happiest: Speakers 4 + 5
  Least happy: Speaker 2

5B

1 GRAMMAR

a 2 wettest 3 furthest 4 worst 5 ugliest
  6 safest 7 most exciting 8 friendliest

b 2 the most interesting 3 most expensive
  4 best 5 busiest

c 2 That's the fastest car I've ever driven
  3 It's the most beautiful building we've
    ever seen
  4 That's the healthiest meal he's ever eaten
  5 It's the best photograph you've ever taken
  6 This is the most exciting sport I've
    ever done
  7 That's the worst flight we've ever had
  8 This is the most interesting city I've
    ever visited

2 VOCABULARY

a 2 coast 3 west 4 population 5 famous

b 2 polluted 3 safe 4 noisy 5 boring
  6 crowded

c 2 town hall 3 castle 4 statue

3 PRONUNCIATION

a 2 crowded 3 dangerous 4 exciting
  5 frightening 6 generous 7 interesting
  8 polluted 9 romantic

4 LISTENING

a 1, 2, 4, 6

b 2 F 3 F 4 T 5 F

5C

1 VOCABULARY

a 2 illness 3 skin 4 faces 5 bones
  6 prevent 7 brain

2 GRAMMAR

a 2 a few 3 many 4 much 5 a little
  6 much 7 many 8 A little 9 a lot of
  10 a few

b 2 tall enough 3 too much 4 enough time
  5 too much 6 too many 7 enough exercise
  8 sleep enough

3 PRONUNCIATION

a 1 much, none 2 few, food, too
  3 diet, like, quite 4 any, healthy, many

4 READING

a potatoes

b 2 F 3 F 4 T 5 F 6 F 7 T

5 LISTENING

a Alice is 35. Her body age is 31.

b 2 no 3 any 4 a lot of 5 positive
  6 a little 7 a few 8 enough

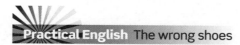
Practical English The wrong shoes

1 VOCABULARY

2 d 3 e 4 a 5 b

2 TAKING SOMETHING BACK
TO A SHOP

2 bought 3 problem 4 afraid 5 size
6 small 7 medium 8 see 9 sorry
10 refund 11 changing rooms 12 receipt

3 SOCIAL ENGLISH

2 Oh, you know. Working! But it was OK.
3 Why don't we go out for dinner? I could
  book a restaurant.
4 OK. For what time?
5 Eight o'clock?
6 Can we make it a bit earlier? Say, seven
  thirty?
7 OK. I'll go and have a shower then.
8 Sure.

4 READING

a 2 Tiffany & Co 3 Ricky's 4 Ricky's

b 1 keyboard 2 pricey 3 accessories
  4 engagement 5 huge 6 do-it-yourself

6A

1 GRAMMAR

a 2 won't win 3 won't remember
  4 'll forget 5 won't sell 6 'll miss

2 VOCABULARY

2 learn 3 'll pass 4 Pull 5 broken
6 borrow 7 lose 8 turn on 9 sent
10 found

4 READING

a 2 Gemini 3 Aries 4 Aquarius 5 Taurus

5 LISTENING

a Matt's star sign is Capricorn and Amy's star
  sign is Virgo.

b 2 M 3 A 4 A 5 M 6 M 7 M

6B

1 GRAMMAR

a 2 Shall I lend you some money
  3 I'll have the chicken
  4 Shall I take your coat
  5 Shall I turn off the air conditioning?
  6 I won't be late

b 2 P 3 O 4 O 5 D 6 P

2 VOCABULARY

2 pay 3 come 4 take 5 give 6 send

3 PRONUNCIATION

a 2 (decide), email, promise
  3 practise, listen, (repair)
  4 borrow, (forget), (agree)
  5 sunbathe, (invite), (complain)

4 READING

a Paul learnt not to lend money to strangers.

b a 6 b 3 c 5 e 4 f 2 g 8 h 7

5 LISTENING

a They had problems with crime.

b Speaker 2 A   Speaker 3 C   Speaker 4 B
  Speaker 5 E

6C

1 GRAMMAR

a 2 do … go, read
  3 will win, 'll lose
  4 were … doing, was watching
  5 Have … dreamt, 've … had
  6 are … doing, 'm reading
  7 Did … sleep, woke up
  8 are … leaving, going to go

b 2 have done 3 works 4 's studying
  5 has … published 6 helped 7 chose
  8 discovered 9 had 10 saw
  11 were watching

2 VOCABULARY

2 with 3 for 4 at 5 to 6 in 7 of 8 from

3 PRONUNCIATION

a 2 now 3 borrow 4 down

4 LISTENING

a 2 You are falling. 3 You are lost.
  4 You are flying. 5 You can't escape.

b Dream 2 a Dream 3 d Dream 4 c
  Dream 5 b

7A

1 GRAMMAR

a 2 to see 3 not to finish 4 to find
5 not to tell 6 not to do 7 to rent

b 2 difficult to talk 3 easy to buy
4 important not to say 5 great to hear
6 fun to be 7 kind to invite

c 2 to study 3 to book 4 to make 5 to get
6 to take

d 2 when to call 3 how many to buy
4 where to go 5 what to study
6 how much to take

2 VOCABULARY

2 offered 3 didn't want 4 pretended
5 needed 6 promised 7 planned
8 forgot / didn't remember 9 forgot /
didn't remember 10 tried 11 learned

4 READING

a The writer is generally positive about
mothers-in-law.

b 2 b 3 a 4 c

5 LISTENING

a no

b 2 J 3 D 4 D 5 J 6 D 7 D 8 J

7B

1 GRAMMAR

a 2 playing 3 studying 4 writing
5 snowing 6 going 7 swimming
8 getting 9 listening 10 using, not driving

b 2 a 3 e 4 f 5 d 6 b

c 3 imagining 4 driving 5 listening
6 Staying 7 reading 8 getting up
9 taking 10 going 11 exercising
12 having 13 Turning 14 leaving

d 2 to use 3 buying 4 to carry 5 travelling
6 to read 7 to look for 8 to show
9 reading 10 looking 11 not to lose
12 to borrow 13 to lend 14 reading
15 to take 16 to charge

2 VOCABULARY

2 e 3 b 4 a 5 d 6 f

3 PRONUNCIATION

a 2 promise 3 surprise 4 engine

4 LISTENING

a one

b Speaker 2 D Speaker 3 A Speaker 4 E
Speaker 5 B

7C

1 GRAMMAR

a 1 don't have to, have to
2 Do … have to, have to
3 Do … have to, don't have to, have to
4 Does … have to, doesn't have to, has to

b 2 You must 3 You mustn't 4 You mustn't
5 You must 6 You mustn't

c 2 mustn't 3 mustn't 4 don't have to
5 mustn't 6 don't have to

2 VOCABULARY

2 quite difficult to understand
American films
3 new teacher speaks very fast
4 of those students are a bit unfriendly
5 English books is a really good idea
6 incredibly hard to learn Chinese

4 READING

a Students' own answers.

b 2 Luis 3 Kiko 4 Josef 5 Gloria 6 Paolo

5 LISTENING

a On all Mac computers, iPhones, the iPod
touch and the iPad.

b 2 around 3,000 3 8,000 4 290,000
5 2006

Practical English At the pharmacy

1 VOCABULARY

2 cold 3 bad stomach 4 temperature
5 headache 6 cough

2 GOING TO A PHARMACY

2 well 3 symptoms 4 have 5 allergic
6 better 7 take 8 every 9 often 10 much

3 SOCIAL ENGLISH

1 lovely, glad 2 Can, for 3 should, sure

4 READING

2 C 3 A 4 I 5 H 6 G 7 F 8 B 9 D

8A

1 GRAMMAR

a 2 should, F 3 shouldn't, E 4 shouldn't, A
5 should, C 6 shouldn't, D

b 2 shouldn't drink 3 should go
4 should see 5 should tell
6 shouldn't give 7 should call

c B 4 C 1 D 7 E 6 F 2 G 5

2 VOCABULARY

2 gets home 3 got lost 4 get fit
5 getting worse 6 got tickets 7 get on
8 got, text message 9 getting up
10 get, school

3 PRONUNCIATION

a 2 could 3 soup 4 book

4 LISTENING

a two

b Speaker 2 B Speaker 3 D Speaker 4 E
Speaker 5 A

8B

1 GRAMMAR

a 2 e 3 a 4 f 5 b 6 d

b 2 see 3 use 4 won't get 5 don't take
6 doesn't work 7 will be 8 isn't

c 2 hang, 'll bring, C
3 walk, 'll have, F
4 throw, make, will come, A
5 's, catch, won't be, G
6 break, 'll have, B
7 see, runs, 'll go, E

2 VOCABULARY

a 2 lost, missed 3 tell, says
4 waiting, hope 5 watching, look at
6 known, met 7 borrow, lend
8 looking for, found 9 wearing, carrying
10 take, bring

4 LISTENING

a five

b 2 In May and June.
3 Extra nights in a hotel if you can't fly home.
4 Things will only get worse.
5 Your family and friends at home.
6 What they will do if there is a natural
disaster.

8C

1 GRAMMAR

a 2 yours
3 Whose laptop is that, his
4 Whose keys are those, hers
5 Whose car is that, ours
6 Whose coats are those, yours
7 Whose house is that, theirs

b 2 yours, ours 3 his, His 4 ours, theirs
5 Your, Mine, hers

2 VOCABULARY
2 quietly   3 seriously   4 lazily
5 dreamily   6 calmly

3 PRONUNCIATION
a 2 <u>di</u>stance   3 <u>do</u>llar   4 ad<u>van</u>tage
5 en<u>joy</u>   6 com<u>ple</u>tely   7 re<u>mem</u>ber
8 <u>pro</u>mise   9 sus<u>pi</u>cious

4 READING
a Students' own answers.

b 2 G   3 D   4 H   5 J

5 LISTENING
a The experiment hoped to find out
if men and women cook differently.
It wasn't successful.

b 2 F   3 T   4 F   5 F   6 T

9A

1 GRAMMAR
a 2 e   3 a   4 c   5 b   6 d

b 2 would you do if you found a million euros
3 a phone if he could afford one
4 gave me caviar I wouldn't eat it
5 would you say if you could talk to the
president
6 look for a new job if I were you

c 2 saw, would scream
3 wouldn't have, didn't have
4 wasn't, would get
5 lived, would learn
6 would … do, attacked

2 VOCABULARY
a Across: 2 cow   6 jellyfish   7 whale
9 bear   10 snake
Down: 3 spider   4 bee   5 sheep   8 horse

3 PRONUNCIATION
a 2 <u>ca</u>mel   3 <u>chi</u>cken   4 <u>cro</u>codile   5 <u>dol</u>phin
6 <u>e</u>lephant   7 gi<u>raffe</u>   8 <u>je</u>llyfish   9 <u>li</u>on
10 <u>mon</u>key   11 mos<u>qui</u>to   12 <u>ra</u>bbit
13 <u>spi</u>der   14 <u>ti</u>ger

4 READING
a Students' own answers.

b 2

5 LISTENING
a By pressing his fingers into the shark's eye.

b 1 Australia
2 Fishing
3 His head, shoulders, and one of his arms.
4 Metal
5 His son
6 By helicopter
7 He had deep cuts all over his body and a
broken nose.
8 Over three metres long

9B

1 VOCABULARY
a 2 claustrophobia d   3 arachnophobia a
4 glossophobia e   5 acrophobia c

b 2 scared   3 fear   4 terrified   5 afraid
6 phobia

2 GRAMMAR
a 2 since   3 since   4 for   5 for
6 since   7 for   8 since

b 2 since   3 since   4 for   5 since   6 Since
7 for   8 since   9 since

c 2 How long has … played
3 How long has … lived
4 How long has … had
5 When did … hear

d 2 ✗ How long
3 ✓
4 ✗ since February
5 ✗ have you had
6 ✗ for eight years
7 ✓
8 ✓

4 LISTENING
a a fear of dogs

b 2 c   3 a   4 c

9C

1 VOCABULARY
2 d   3 b   4 f   5 e   6 h   7 g   8 a

2 GRAMMAR
a 2 sent   3 she met   4 They fell   5 they got
6 They had   7 They moved   8 they've lived
9 has just put   10 he's been   11 have made

b 2 did … get, 've been
3 has … worked, finished
4 have … had, bought
5 did … meet, 's known
6 have … lived, arrived

3 PRONUNCIATION
a 1 married, primary, secondary, separate
2 divorced, musician, retire, successful

4 READING
a A 7   B 2   C 6   D 3   E 5   G 4

b 2 did his mother buy
3 were
4 did John Lennon die
5 has Julian Lennon made
6 has Sean Lennon played

5 LISTENING
a They were both two years old.

b 2 F   3 T   4 T   5 T   6 T   7 T   8 F

1 VOCABULARY
2 straight   3 round   4 exit   5 lights
6 take   7 left   8 right

2 ASKING HOW TO GET THERE
2 Could you say that again?
3 How many stops is that?
4 OK. And then?
5 Where is it?
6 OK. Thanks. See you later.

3 SOCIAL ENGLISH
2 said   3 don't   4 stay   5 feel   6 long
7 think

4 READING
2 30–40 minutes   3 $14   4 $45
5 nothing   6 6.30 a.m.   7 $13

10A

1 VOCABULARY
a 2 given   3 discovered   4 used   5 played
6 shown   7 called   8 invented   9 opened
10 based

2 GRAMMAR
a 2 The film *The Iron Lady* is based on the
life of Margaret Thatcher
3 Mobile phones weren't invented by Apple
4 Lead isn't used in petrol nowadays
5 Low-cost flights are sold online
6 The Petronus Towers were designed by
an Argentinian architect
7 *Avatar* wasn't directed by Steven Spielberg
8 Minis aren't made by a British company
any more

b 2 Contact lenses were invented by a Czech
chemist
3 Where are olives grown
4 The VW Beetle was designed in the 1930s
5 Diamonds are found in many different
colours
6 When were vitamins discovered
7 Spanish is spoken in Spain and many
parts of South America
8 Where were the *Lord of the Rings* films
made

c 2 are worn by people of all ages
3 weren't invented by Microsoft
4 the heating controlled by a computer
5 was written by Stieg Larsson
6 aren't used by people very much today
7 wasn't painted by Picasso
8 the Harry Potter films directed by the
same person

3 PRONUNCIATION

a 2 checked 3 wanted 4 rained 5 decided

4 LISTENING

a 2 c 3 a

b 2 in Percy Spencer's pocket, not on the table.
3 German, not American
4 glass and paper, not water and air.
5 the man's wife's hand, not his hand
6 potato chips, not crisps
7 a chef, not a waiter
8 'Saratoga chips', not 'Saratoga potatoes'

10B

1 VOCABULARY

a 2 h 3 e 4 b 5 a 6 f 7 i 8 d 9 g

b 2 g 3 c 4 a 5 b 6 i 7 f 8 d 9 e

2 GRAMMAR

a 2 I didn't use to behave
3 We used to wear
4 Did Alex use to have
5 didn't use to study
6 used to be
7 didn't use to play
8 Did your teachers use to give

b 2 He used to go
3 We didn't use to understand
4 Did you use to
5 School used to
6 Did your friends use to help

4 READING

a 2 What's the most important lesson
you learned at school?
3 Did you ever behave badly?
4 What subjects were you good at?
5 What did you want to do when you left
school?
6 Did you have a favourite teacher?

b 2 T 3 F 4 F 5 T 6 T 7 T 8 F

5 LISTENING

a Amy was good at languages at school, but
Tony wasn't.

b 2 studied it at university
3 some numbers
4 too uncomfortable
5 German
6 make younger pupils learn languages

10C

1 GRAMMAR

a 2 might go 3 might have 4 might take
5 might rain 6 might invite 7 might make
8 might eat

b 2 might not get 3 might have
4 might not come 5 might not be
6 might miss 7 might go 8 might fail

2 VOCABULARY

a 3 decision 4 die 5 education 6 elect
7 imagination 8 inform 9 invitation
10 live 11 option 12 organize 13 succeed

b 2 decision 3 invite 4 Success 5 inform
6 decided 7 imagine 8 life

3 PRONUNCIATION

a 2 ✓ 3 ✗ 4 ✗ 5 ✗ 6 ✓ 7 ✗ 8 ✓

4 READING

a To discover if a good night's sleep helps when
you have to make an important decision.

b 2 at different times 3 some time later
4 Some 5 four 6 different 7 lost
8 REM sleep

5 LISTENING

a two

b Speaker 2 D Speaker 3 A Speaker 4 E
Speaker 5 B

11A

1 VOCABULARY

a 2 track 3 match point, serve 4 bunker
5 lap 6 penalty 7 corner

b 1 into 2 round 3 into 4 out of
5 towards 6 past 7 to, into

c Across: 4 down 5 up 7 towards 8 across
Down: 1 out of 2 round 3 into 6 past
7 through 8 along

2 GRAMMAR

a 2 kicked, under 3 went through
4 threw, into 5 ran across 6 hit, over

b 2 out of 3 to 4 into 5 along 6 under
7 past 8 through 9 along 10 towards
11 across

3 PRONUNCIATION

a 2 volleyball 3 motor racing 4 skiing
5 windsurfing 6 cycling 7 basketball
8 rugby 9 athletics

4 LISTENING

a cards, tennis, football, board games,
basketball

b 2 Speaker 5 3 Speaker 1 4 Speaker 4
5 Speaker 3

11B

1 VOCABULARY

a 2 over 3 after 4 off 5 in 6 on

b 2 throw away 3 turn up 4 look up
5 look forward to 6 get on with 7 go out
8 try on 9 take back 10 give up

2 GRAMMAR

a 2 pay it back 3 look for them 4 ✓
5 looks after my kids 6 ✓

b 2 She'll give them back on Friday
3 Are you looking forward to it
4 I called her back when I got home
5 We don't get on with them
6 Shall we turn it on

4 READING

a 2 get up 3 go out 4 take off 5 put on
6 give up 7 turn on 8 write down

b 1 ✓ 2 ✗ 3 ✗ 4 ✗ 5 ✗ 6 ✗ 7 ✓ 8 ✗
9 ✓ 10 ✓

5 LISTENING

a positive

b 2 T 3 F 4 F 5 T 6 T

11C

1 GRAMMAR

a 2 Neither was I 3 So do I 4 So would I
5 So am I 6 Neither have I

b 2 So did I 3 Neither have I 4 So was I
5 Neither am I 6 Neither can I
7 So would I 8 Neither do I

2 VOCABULARY

2 as 3 like 4 both 5 so 6 neither
7 identical

3 PRONUNCIATION

c 2 <u>si</u>milar 3 co<u>in</u>cidence 4 a<u>ma</u>zing
5 dis<u>co</u>ver 6 <u>e</u>verywhere 7 perso<u>na</u>lity
8 <u>de</u>finitely

4 READING

a 1

b 2 F 3 F 4 T 5 T 6 F

5 LISTENING

a 2 a   3 b

b 2 KB   3 OT   4 KB   5 RR   6 OT

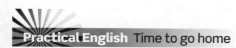

Practical English Time to go home

1 ON THE PHONE

a 2 sorry, wrong
3 line, busy, leave, message, call, back
4 put

2 SOCIAL ENGLISH

a 2 great news   3 go first   4 later
5 Never better

3 READING

a 2

b 2 f   3 i   4 e   5 d   6 b   7 m   8 g   9 j
10 k   11 a   12 l   13 h

12A

1 GRAMMAR

a 2 hadn't closed   3 had started
4 hadn't flown   5 had read   6 hadn't heard

b 2 Had they eaten sushi before
3 Had he won a medal before
4 Had they made a cake before
5 Had she run a marathon before
6 Had you been there before

c 2 had done the ironing, he put the
clothes away
3 they had watched the news, they turned
off the TV
4 I had read the book, I gave it back
5 had tried on the top, she went to the
checkout
6 we had had dinner, we did the washing up

d 2 opened   3 had broken   4 had already left
5 hadn't stolen   6 hadn't lost   7 had seen
8 had left   9 had put

2 PRONUNCIATION

a 2 We'd lost it.   3 You'd seen her.
4 It'd been a terrible day.   5 I hadn't sent it.
6 She hadn't done it.   7 They hadn't told me.

3 VOCABULARY

a 2 put   3 belonged   4 left   5 gone on
6 got out of   7 had   8 realized   9 was
10 got on

4 LISTENING

a A 2   C 4   D 3

b 2 30 hours (not 13)
3 Zambia (not Kenya)
4 swum to safety (not walked)
5 cooking (not washing up)
6 too small (not big)
7 living room (not kitchen).
8 Mrs Dodd's husband (not Mrs Dodd)

12B

1 GRAMMAR

a 2 didn't like her parents
3 was getting divorced
4 'd been to the police station
5 hadn't met his girlfriend
6 'd seen James with another woman
7 couldn't cook
8 wouldn't tell anyone
9 'd speak to her tomorrow / the next day
10 'd got a lot of work to do

b 2 I want a cup of coffee
3 We haven't seen the new neighbours yet
4 I don't want to go to the cinema
5 We'll go to the party
6 My computer has just broken
7 The city is very old
8 We'll visit you

2 VOCABULARY

a 2 told   3 told   4 said   5 told   6 said   7 told
8 told   9 said   10 said

b 2 told   3 told   4 said   5 told   6 said
7 said   8 said   9 told   10 told

3 PRONUNCIATION

a 2 married   3 letter   4 middle   5 hurry
6 different   7 sorry   8 summer
9 message   10 happy

4 LISTENING

a Jess gossips, but Alan doesn't.

b 2 F   3 F   4 F   5 T   6 T   7 T   8 F

12C

1 GRAMMAR

a 2 a   3 a   4 b   5 b   6 a   7 a   8 b

b b 4   c 5   d 1   e 6   f 8   g 2   h 7

c 2 did Spain win
3 did REM stay
4 plays
5 did Amy Winehouse die
6 do polar bears live
7 roads join
8 produces the most bananas

2 VOCABULARY

a 2 overweight – It isn't used to describe
personality.
3 tracksuit – It isn't an item of jewellery.
4 a phone call – It doesn't use the verb 'do'.
5 exciting – It isn't a negative word.
6 town hall – It isn't somewhere you can
do shopping.
7 finish – It isn't a verb that can be followed
by 'to'.
8 get up – It isn't a use of 'get' which means
'become'.
9 bat – It isn't an insect.

b 2 on   3 back   4 out / away   5 to
6 forward   7 into / across   8 in   9 on
10 up

c 2 stay   3 fall   4 make   5 do   6 lend
7 spend   8 get   9 earn   10 find

3 PRONUNCIATION

a 2 school   3 hope   4 turn   5 bald
6 towel   7 thin   8 horse   9 word   10 wear
11 fear   12 city   13 chemist's   14 forget

4 READING

a 2 G   3 J   4 C   5 H   6 D   7 F   8 A
9 I   10 B

5 LISTENING

a 1 mind   2 Sport   3 Call   4 Millionaire
5 Pop

b Speaker 2 C   Speaker 3 D   Speaker 4 B
Speaker 5 A

UNIVERSITY PRESS

Great Clarendon Street, Oxford, OX2 6DP, United Kingdom

Oxford University Press is a department of the University of Oxford.
It furthers the University's objective of excellence in research, scholarship,
and education by publishing worldwide. Oxford is a registered trade
mark of Oxford University Press in the UK and in certain other countries

© Oxford University Press 2012

The moral rights of the author have been asserted

First published in 2012

2019

21

ISBN: 978 0 19 459822 4

Printed in China
This book is printed on paper from certified and well-managed sources

ACKNOWLEDGEMENTS

*The authors would like to thank all the teachers and students round the world whose
feedback has helped us shape* English File.

The authors would also like to thank: all those at Oxford University Press (both
in Oxford and around the world) and the design team who have contributed
their skills and ideas to producing this course.

*Finally very special thanks from Clive to Maria Angeles, Lucia, and Eric, and from
Christina to Cristina, for all their support and encouragement. Christina would also like
to thank her children Joaquin, Marco, and Krysia for their constant inspiration.*

*The authors and publishers are grateful to the following who have given permission to
reproduce the following extracts and adaptations of copyright material*: p.9 Extract
from 'Fleurs Fraîches' by Heidi Ellison, 19 October 2010. © Heidi Ellison,
ParisUpdate.com. Reproduced by permission; p.16 Extract from 'My loaf
saver: Woman's life is saved by bag of sliced white bread as it stops her head
smashing against crashed car' by Luke Salkeld, *The Daily Mail*, 26 November
2011. Reproduced by permission of Solo Syndication; p.16 Extract from 'Man's
life saved by heroic DVD', www.metro.co.uk. Reproduced by permission of
Solo Syndication; p.25 Extract from 'Research: women will be doing the
housework until 2050' by Tim Ross, *The Telegraph*, 20 May 2011. © Telegraph
Media Group Limited 2011; p.40 Extract from 'Tourist Scam Alert'. © 2012
www.ricksteves.com, used with permission; p.44 Extract from 'Mothers-in-
law are lovely in their place. Their own place, that is' by Luisa Dillner, *The
Independent*, 28 February 2010. Reproduced by permission; p.46 Extract from
'Apple Teams Up To Use iPhone To Save Cherokee Language' by Murray Evans.
Reproduced by permission of Associated Press; p.66 Extract from 'David
Suchet remembers his school sporting achievements and the teacher who
inspired him to pursue acting' by Tim Oglethorpe, *The Daily Mail Weekend
Magazine*, 24 October 2009. Reproduced by permission of Solo Syndication;
p.66 Extract from 'Bonjour is about all we learn from 5 years of French' by
Laura Clark, *The Daily Mail*, 02 August 2007. Reproduced by permission of Solo
Syndication; p.68 Extract from 'No need to sleep on this one: A good night's
rest really does help you make important decisions', *The Daily Mail*, 20 June
2011. Reproduced by permission of Solo Syndication.

*Although every effort has been made to trace and contact copyright holders before
publication, this has not been possible in some cases. We apologize for any apparent
infringement of copyright and if notified, the publisher will be pleased to rectify any
errors or omissions at the earliest opportunity.*

*The publishers would like to thank the following for their kind permission to reproduce
photographs*: Alamy Images pp.8 (Mediablizimages/dress), 11 (Robert Stainforth/
bluebell wood), 33 (Prisma Bildagentur AG/beach), 33 (Funkyfood London-
Paul Williams/ferry), 48 (Scott Hortop/laptop); Barcroft Media p.74 (Niklas
Hallen/India twins); The Bridgeman Art Library pp.8 and 9 (The Art Institute
of Chicago); Corbis pp.11 (RCWW,Inc/typing, Simon Marcus/passport,
A.Inden/young people), 20 (Tibor Bognar/Vienna Opera house), 23 (Atlantide
Phototravel/soup), 29 (Franz-Peter Tschauner/dpa/monopoly), 32 (John
Warburton Lee/JAI), 48 (Dirk Lindner/i-pod), 55 (TW Photo/Gordon Ramsay),

56 (Wolfgang Kumm/dpa/bee), 61 (Kevin Knight/Julian Lennon), 63 (Andy
Rain/EPA/aeroplanes, Martyn Goddard/mini), 64 (Scott camazine/x-ray); Getty
Images pp.5 (Yellow Dog Productions), 6 (Bartomeu Amengual), 10 (Lester
Lefkowitz), 12 (Kniel Synnatzschke/girl wavy hair, Brad Wilson/girl with dark
curly hair, Gabe Palmer/man curly hair), 15 (Jacob Halaska), 18 (Bloomberg),
20 (Joe Cornish/Prague, Keith MacGregor/Budapest), 23 (Dorling Kindersly/
paella), 29 (PM Images/tidy up), 33 (Walter Bibikow/Zagreb, John and Tina
Reid/Dubrovnik), 35 (Davies and Starr), 38 (Leon), 53 (AFP/earthquake/fire/
hurricane, Esch Collection/blizzard) 55 (Wireimage/Heston Blumenthal,
Delia Smith, Nigella Lawson) 56 (Peter Cade/cow, Paul Souders/jellyfish/
whale, Paul Oomen/bear, Visuals Unlimited, Inc, John Abbott/snake, Suchitra
prints/monkey, Danita Delimont/sheep, Kelly Funk/horse), 58 (TBR), 59 (Nick
Ridley), 60 (Andrew Bret Wallis), 61 (John Lennon, Sean Lennon, Judy Garland,
Liza Minnelli) 62 (Walter Bibikow), 63 (ULTRA.F/Petronus Towers), 64 (Brian
Hagiwara/crisps), 74 (LatitudeStock/Justin Williams/Romulus and Remus,
Kray Brothers), 78 (Ulrik Tofte/girls whispering, Yellow Dog Productions/men
chatting); The Kobal Collection pp.63 (Film 4/*The Iron Lady*, Twentieth Century
Fox/*Avatar*); Oxford University Press pp.8 (Oleksiy Maksymenko Photography/
coat), 11 (Michael Blann/tourists, sunbathing, Alamy/Juice Images/couple with
suitcase), 12 (Getty Images/Kindler Andreas/man with scarf, Getty Images/
Alan Graf/middle-aged woman), 19 (Corbis/Ocean), 20 (Getty Images/Chase
Jarvis/backpacker), 29 (Getty Images/Art Vandalay/juggling, Corbis/Plattform/
Johner Images/baking), 41 (Getty Images/Jose Luis Pelaez Inc), 44 (Alamy/
MBI), 48 (Corbis/Ken Seet/class), 51 (Tom Grill/Tetra Images), 56 (spider),
63 (Saturn, phone, petrol pump), 64 (microwave), 68, 72 (Getty Images/Diane
Diederich), 73 (Getty Images/Scott Markewitz), 75 (Union Jack flag, US flag),
78 (Corbis Premium/backview of women); Reuters p.7 (Aly Song); Rex Features
pp.11 (camping, Sipa Press/ski hire, Dan Callister/hotel reception), 23 (Ben
Pipe/The Travel Library/New York), 26 (FI Online), 36 (Alex Segre), 46 (Geoff
Moore), 48 Alex Segre/kindle 55 (Erik Pendzich/Jamie Oliver), 66 (ITV/David
Suchet), 74 (Billy Farrell Agency/Olsen twins); SWNS p.16 (SWNS.com)

The painting reproduced on pages 8 and 9 is *Sunday Afternoon on the Island of La
Grande Jatte*, 1884–86 (oil on canvas), Seurat, Georges Pierre (1859–91)/The Art
Institute of Chicago, IL, USA/The Bridgeman Art Library

Commissioned photography by: Gareth Boden p.8 (ring, trousers, skirt, track suit,
hat, trainers, belt, tie)

Pronunciation chart artwork by: Ellis Nadler

Illustrations by: Peter Bull pp.47 bottom, 49; Atsushi Hara/Dutch Uncle Agency
pp. 13, 24, 25, 39, 50, 54; Satoshi Hashimoto/Dutch Uncle Agency p.69; Tim
Marrs pp.22, 42; Jérôme Mireault/Colagene Illustrations pp. 28, 31, 40, 70;
Roger Penwill pp.37, 47 top, 71; Kath Walker Illustration pp.16, 17, 45, 52, 69
top, 76, 77

Picture research and illustrations commissioned by: Catherine Blackie

Design by: Stephen Strong